ALL YOU NEED IS A PENCIL AND YOUR IMAGINATION!

Vampire doodles

ILLUSTRATIONS BY
TIM HYNES

V<small>AMPIRE</small> D<small>OODLES</small>

Copyright © 2011 Dalmatian Press, LLC
Published in 2011 by Piggy Toes Press, LLC

Published by Piggy Toes Press,
an imprint of Dalmatian Publishing Group
Atlanta, GA 30329

ISBN10: 161524478-6

11 12 13 HLG36349 9 8 7 6 5 4 3 2

Follow us on Facebook® and Twitter®

Visit our website and browse our other products
www.piggytoespress.com

COOL **Vampire** STYLE

DRAW THE LEATHER JACKET
HE IS WEARING

Love Bites...

DRAW THE VAMPIRE GIRL'S
MOUTH, DON'T FORGET HER FANGS

DESIGN THE REST OF
HIS OUTFIT AND HAIRSTYLE

MAKING
A STATEMENT...

DOODLE A HAIRSTYLE AND
T-SHIRT DESIGN

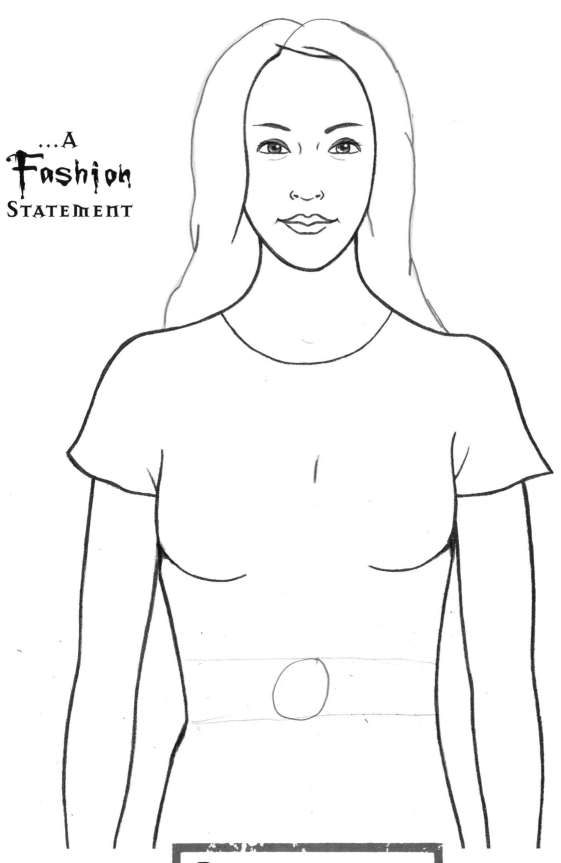

...A **Fashion** Statement

DOODLE A HAIRSTYLE AND
T-SHIRT DESIGN

FRIGHT NIGHT

CREATE A CRAZY HAIRSTYLE
FOR THIS VAMPIRE

PROM NIGHT

SKETCH HER HEAD AND FACE
AND DETAILS ON THE DRESS

FILL IN THE FACIAL DETAILS

...Vampire or Victim?

FILL IN THE FACIAL DETAILS

DOODLE FACES
AND BODIES FOR THE BATS

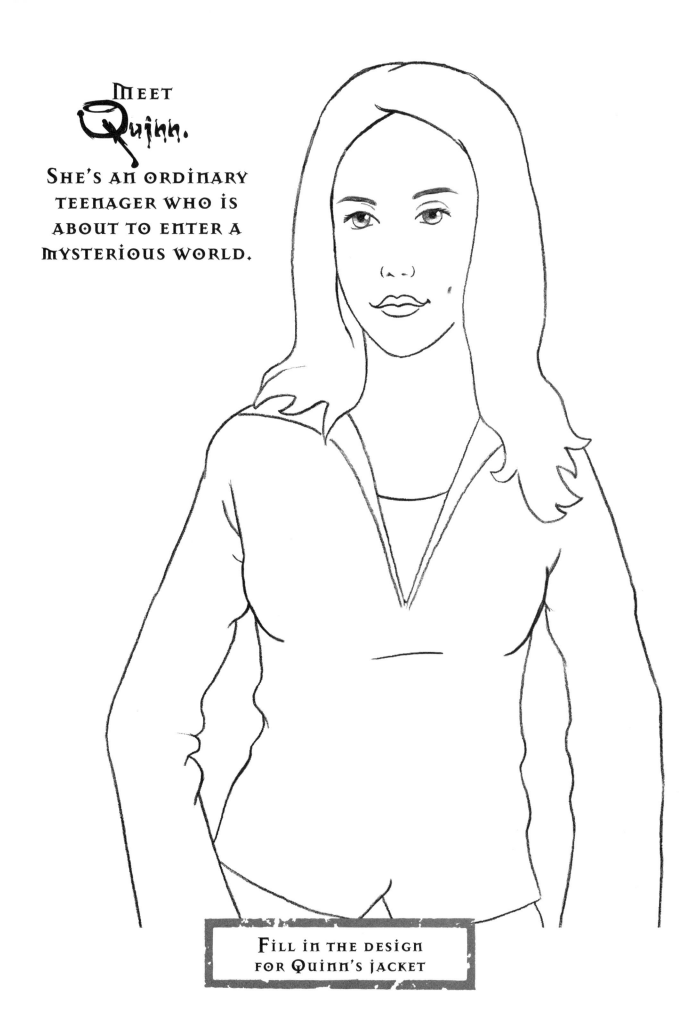

MEET
Quinn.

SHE'S AN ORDINARY TEENAGER WHO IS ABOUT TO ENTER A MYSTERIOUS WORLD.

FILL IN THE DESIGN FOR Quinn's JACKET

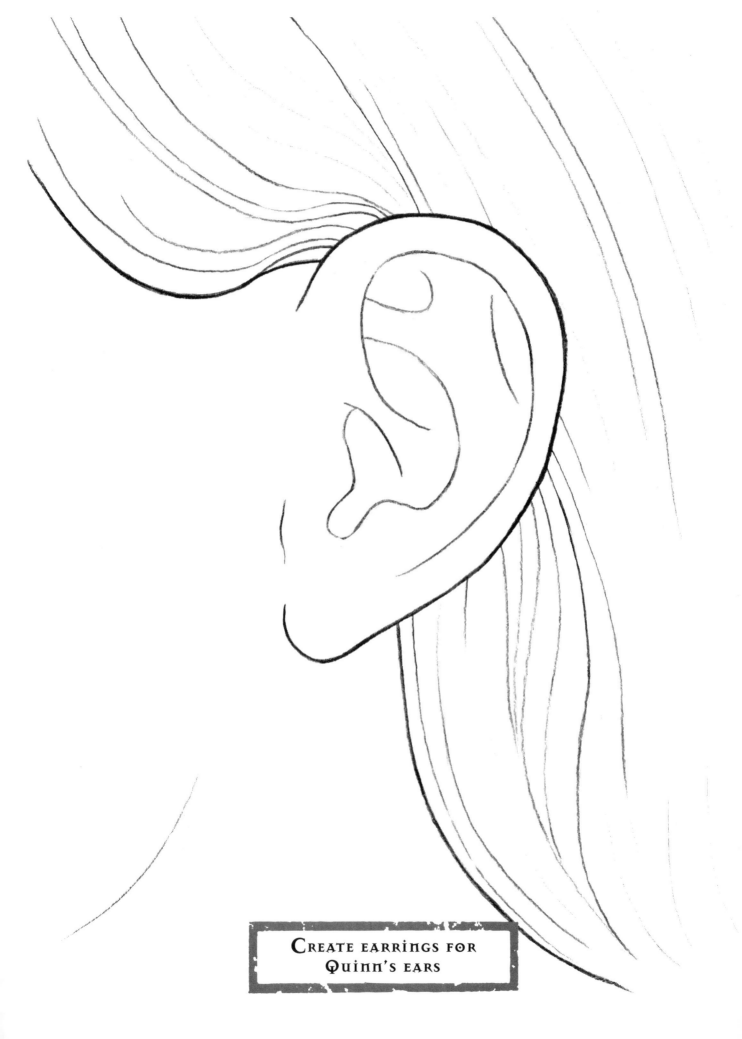

CREATE EARRINGS FOR
Quinn's EARS

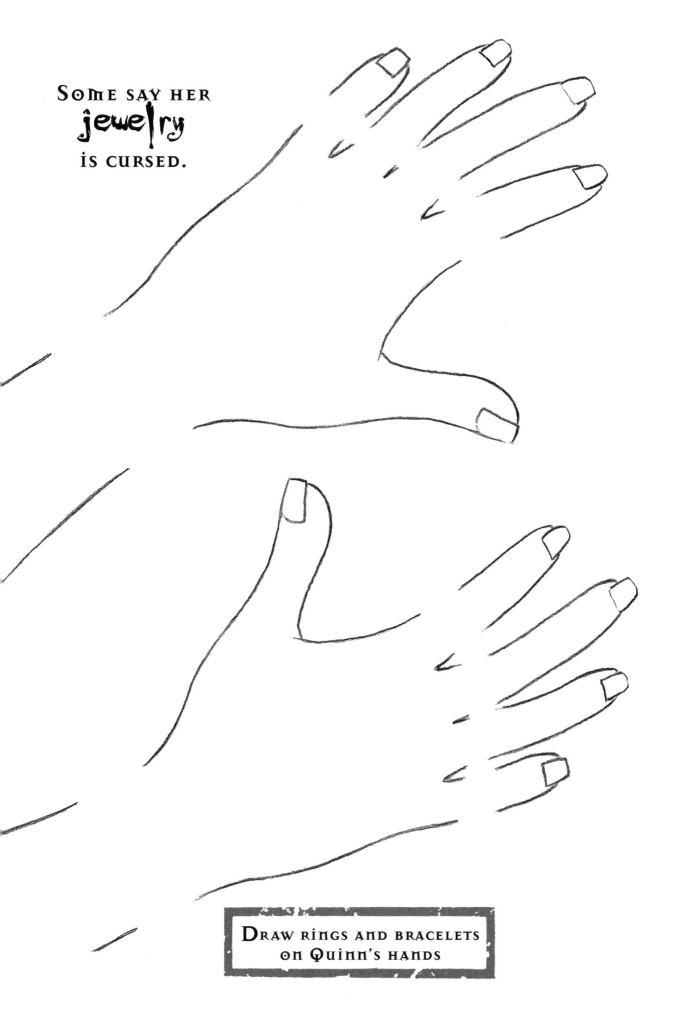

SOME SAY HER *jewelry* IS CURSED.

DRAW RINGS AND BRACELETS ON QUINN'S HANDS

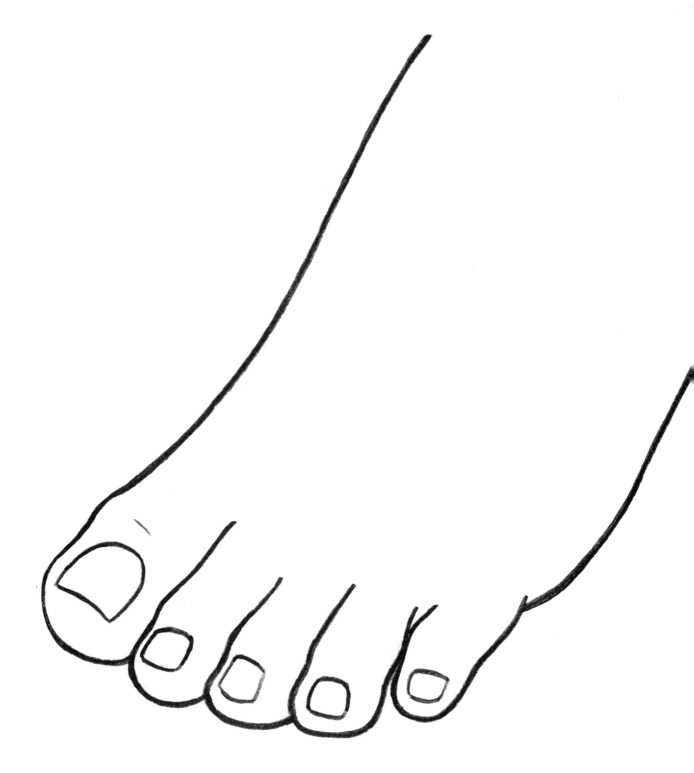

DOODLE SOME TOE RINGS AND
DESIGNS ON HER TOENAILS

DESIGN THE CHARM ON
QUINN'S NECKLACE

COMPLETE THE STAINED GLASS
WINDOW AND SMALL PAINTINGS

DRAW WHAT YOU WOULD FIND ON
Quinn's vanity

DOODLE DESIGNS ON THIS
ANTIQUE LAMP SHADE

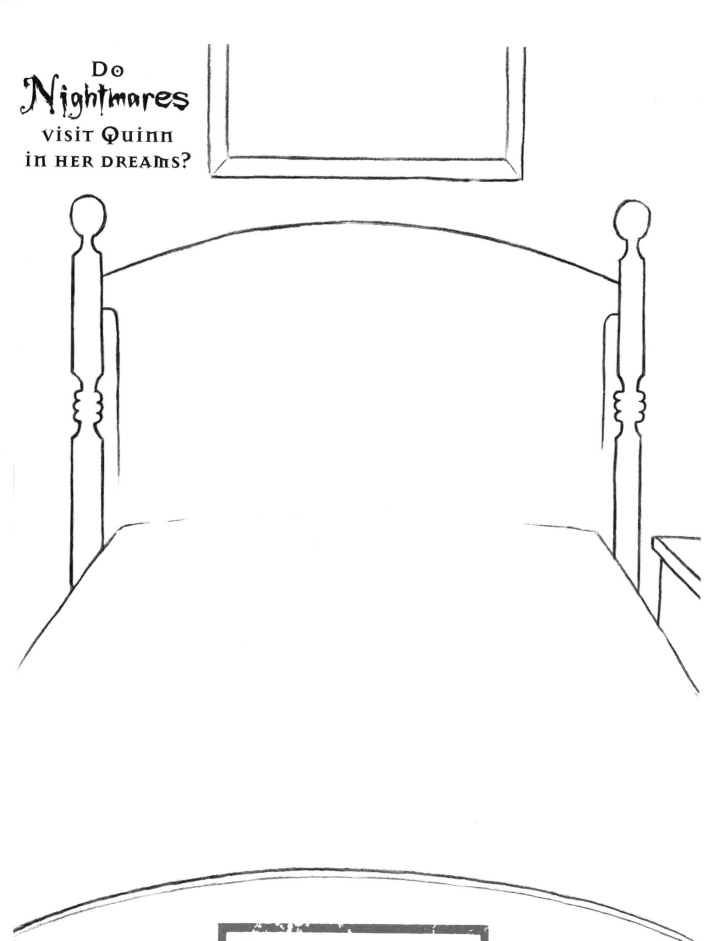

Do **Nightmares** visit Quinn in her dreams?

CREATE SOME PILLOWS AND BLANKET DESIGNS

ARTISTIC ABILITIES

COMPLETE THE DRAWINGS
HANGING IN QUINN'S BEDROOM

WHAT WAKES
Quinn
in the middle
OF THE
Night?

DESIGN HER PAJAMAS AND
BEDROOM SCENE BEHIND HER

ADD DETAILS AND CREATURES TO
THIS EERIE GRAVESITE

COMPLETE THE GATES
TO THE CEMETERY

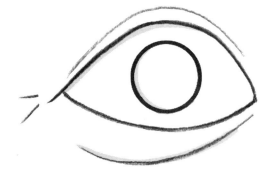

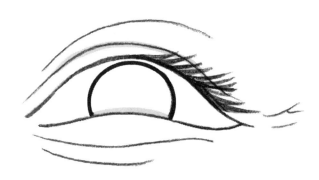

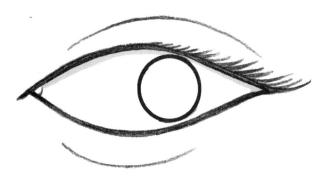

MAKE THE EYES SCARIER

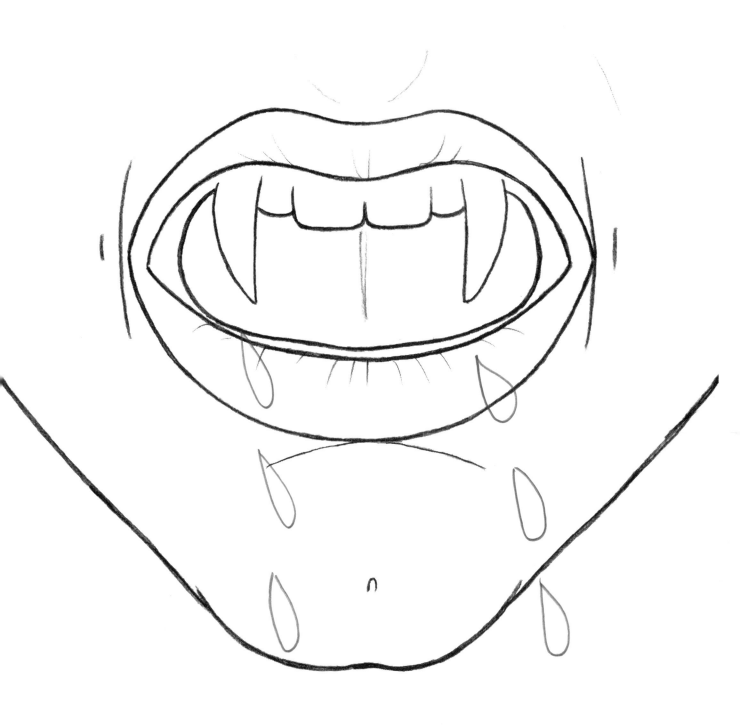

ADD BLOOD DRIPPING
FROM THE FANGS

DRAW A SPOOKY FIGURE IN THE
HALL AND COMPLETE THE PAINTINGS

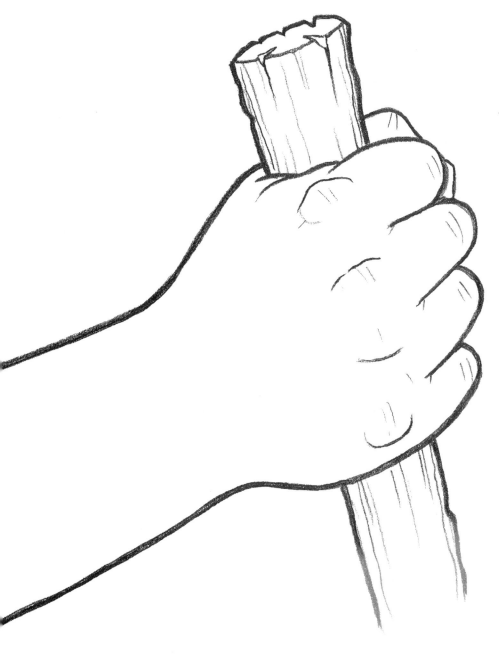

What DO HER DREAMS MEAN? WHY DOES SHE SEE THESE VISIONS?

FINISH DRAWING THE
SLAYER'S WEAPON

CARVE YOUR INITIALS INTO
THE TREE TRUNK AND VAMPIRES
LURKING BEHIND THE TREE

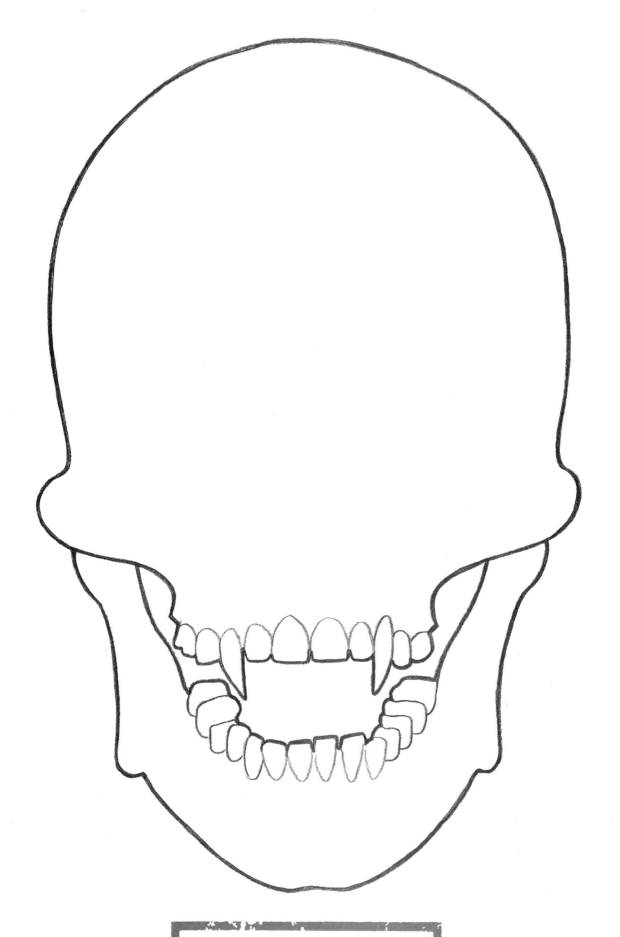

ADD DETAILS AND FEATURES
TO THIS VAMPIRE SKULL

A Vampire Coat of Arms

IMAGES OF AN **ancient** CREST AND CROSSES HAUNT Quinn's DREAM.

DOODLE DESIGNS ON THE CROSSES

SANDS OF TIME

SKETCH IN SAND DROPPING
THROUGH THE HOURGLASS

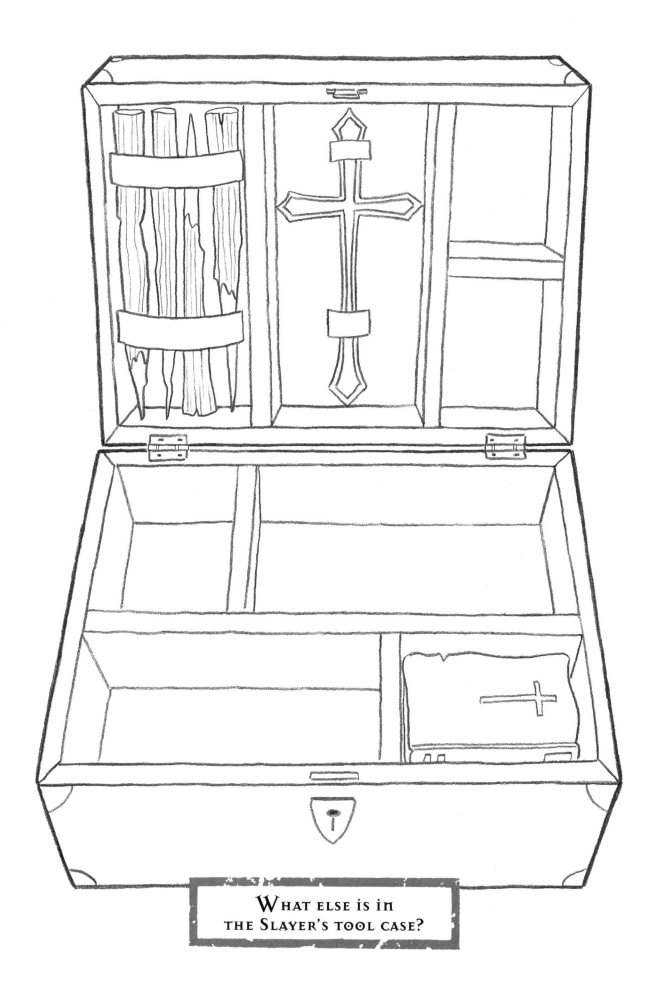

WHAT ELSE IS IN
THE SLAYER'S TOOL CASE?

FINISH DRAWING THE FACE
ON THIS GARGOYLE

DRAW A SCARY GARGOYLE OF
YOUR OWN ON THIS PAGE

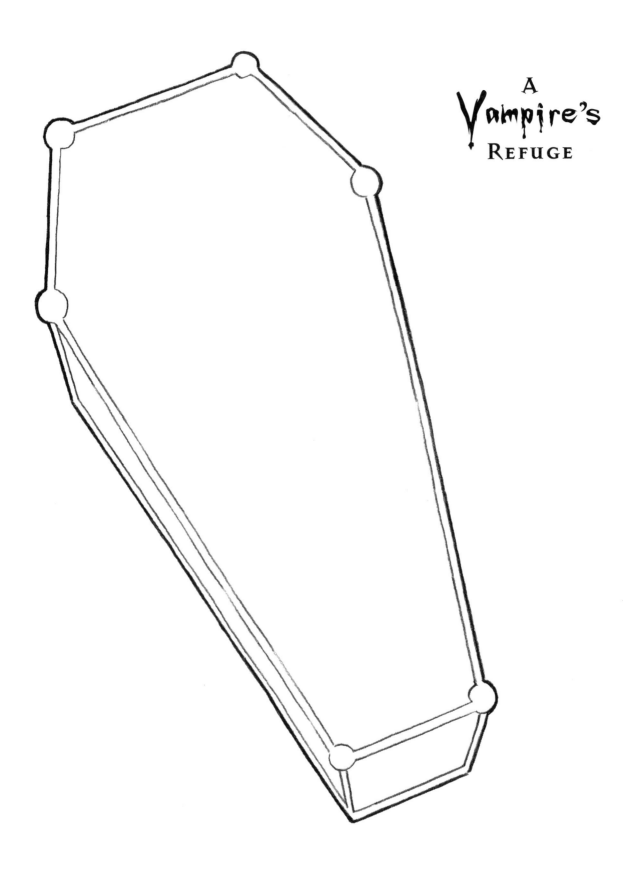

A
Vampire's
REFUGE

DECORATE THE
MYSTERIOUS COFFIN

It's always the
Vision
of the handsome
stranger that
awakens
Quinn from her
dreams

DOODLE A HAIRSTYLE FOR
THE HANDSOME STRANGER

TIME TO HIT THE BOOKS...

SKETCH STUDENTS HEADING INTO THE HIGH SCHOOL

Always in Style

CREATE SOME PATCHES AND
DESIGNS FOR THIS BACKPACK

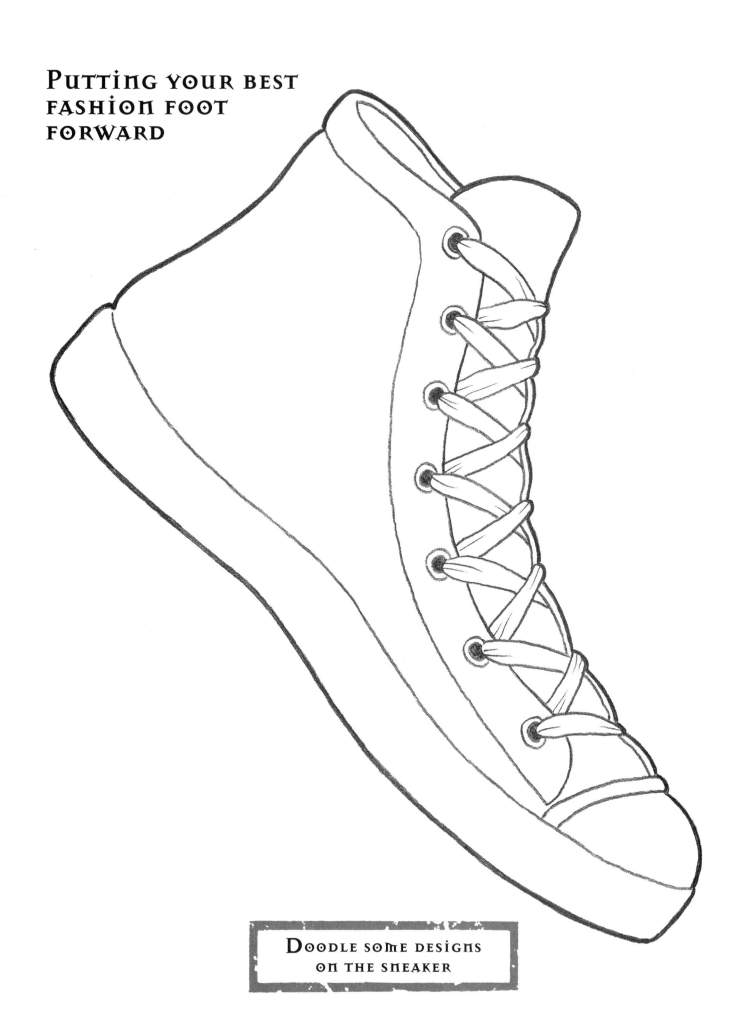

PUTTING YOUR BEST
FASHION FOOT
FORWARD

DOODLE SOME DESIGNS
ON THE SNEAKER

A Cup of Joe in the morning...

PERSONALIZE THIS COFFEE CUP
WITH YOUR OWN ART

FOOD FOR THOUGHT

ADD SILVERWARE AND FOOD
TO THE PLACE SETTING

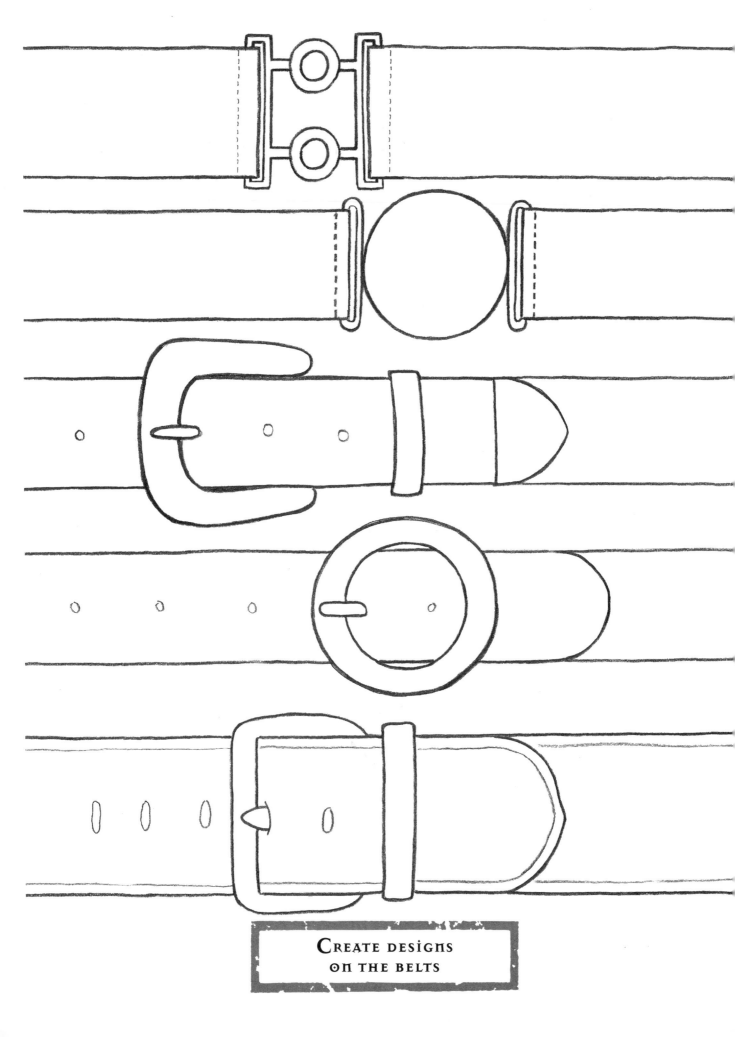

CREATE DESIGNS
ON THE BELTS

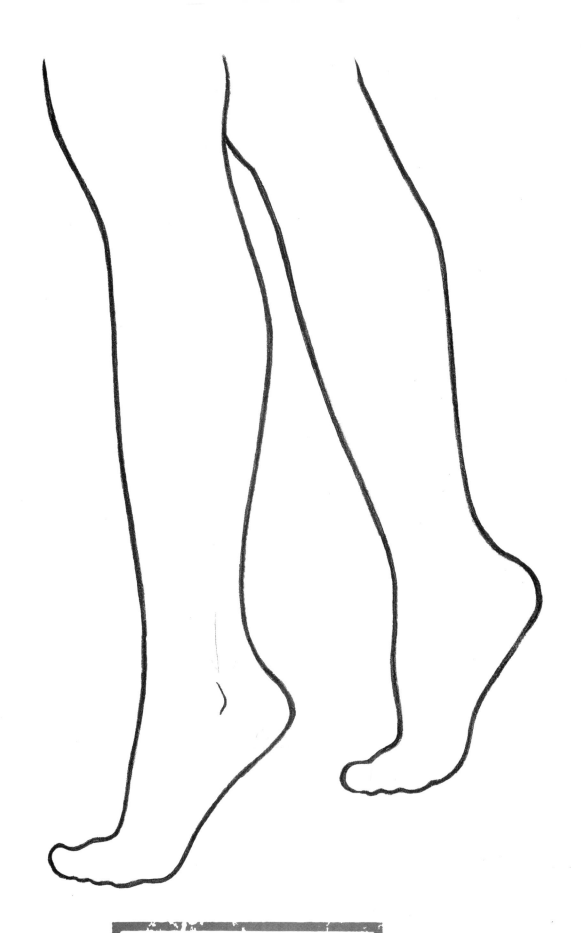

DESIGN HER SHOES AND
PATTERNED TIGHTS

DRAW WHAT YOU THINK
QUINN KEEPS IN HER LOCKER

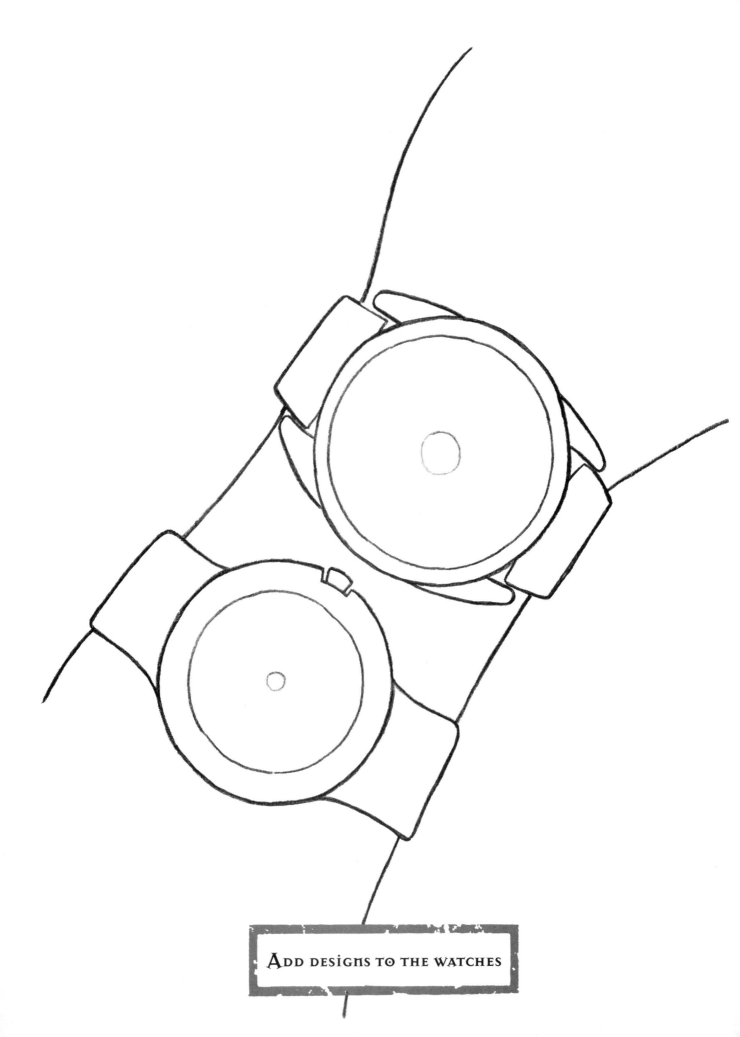

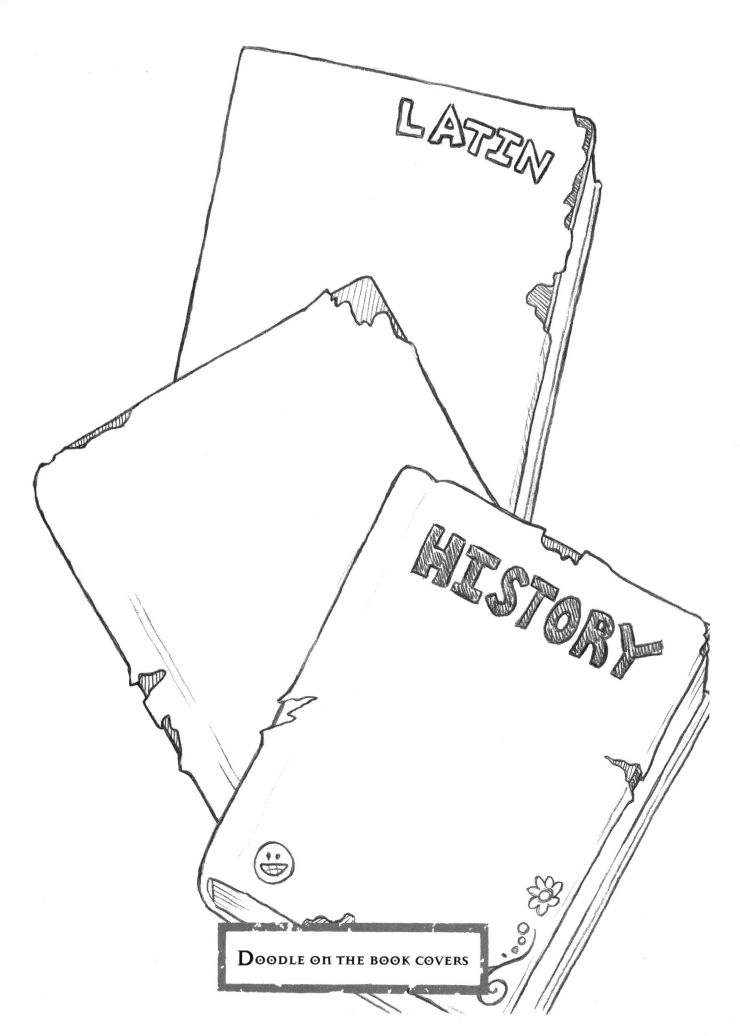

LATIN

HISTORY

DOODLE ON THE BOOK COVERS

QUINN CAN'T FORGET
HER DREAM AND THE
VISION OF THE STRANGER

DRAW SOME IMAGES
FROM QUINN'S DREAMS

DRAW YOURSELF AS
A STUDENT IN THE SCHOOL

Keys to Quinn's secrets...

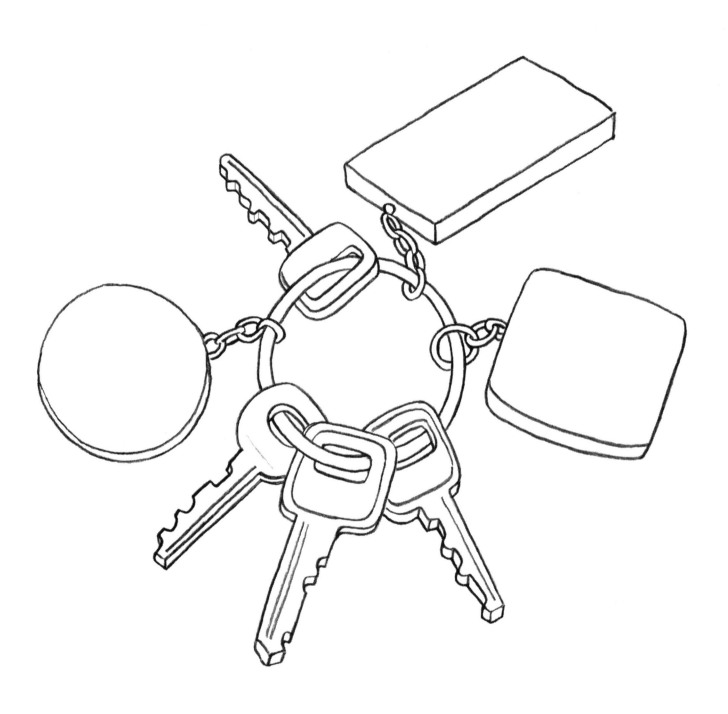

CREATE DESIGNS ON THE KEY FOBS

ADD SOME ICONS OR MESSAGES
TO THE STRANGER'S PHONE

COMPLETE THE STOREFRONT AND ADD MANNEQUINS IN THE WINDOWS

Quinn is **fascinated** BY A BRACELET AND A CANDLE SHE FINDS

DOODLE SOME MORE CHARMS ON THE BRACELET

ADD A FLAME AND SMOKE
TO THE CANDLE

DOODLE SOME DECORATIONS
ON THE SHOPPING BAG

DRAW A BAG FROM
YOUR FAVORITE STORE

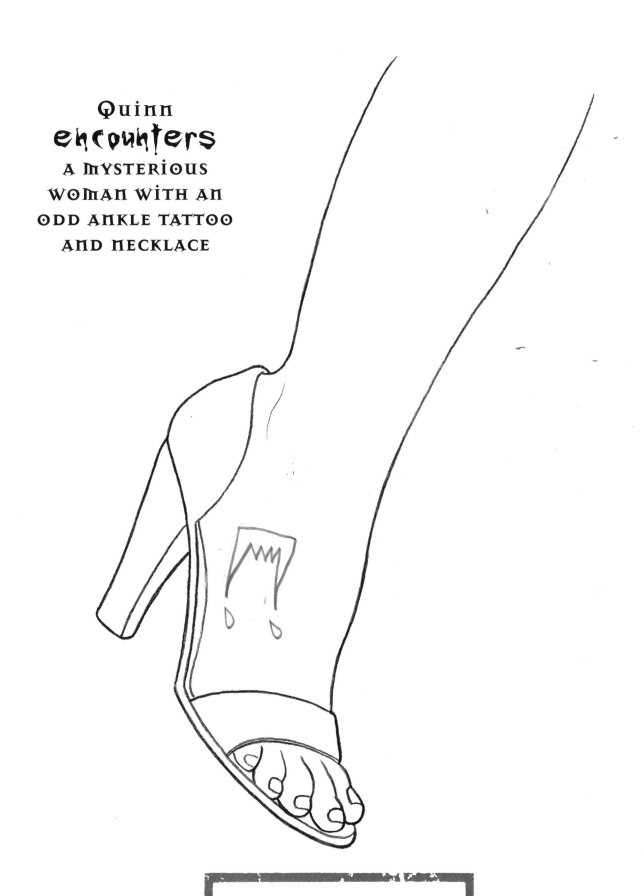

Quinn **encounters** A MYSTERIOUS WOMAN WITH AN ODD ANKLE TATTOO AND NECKLACE

DRAW HER UNIQUE TATTOO

DRAW THE NECKLACE THE
WOMAN WEARS

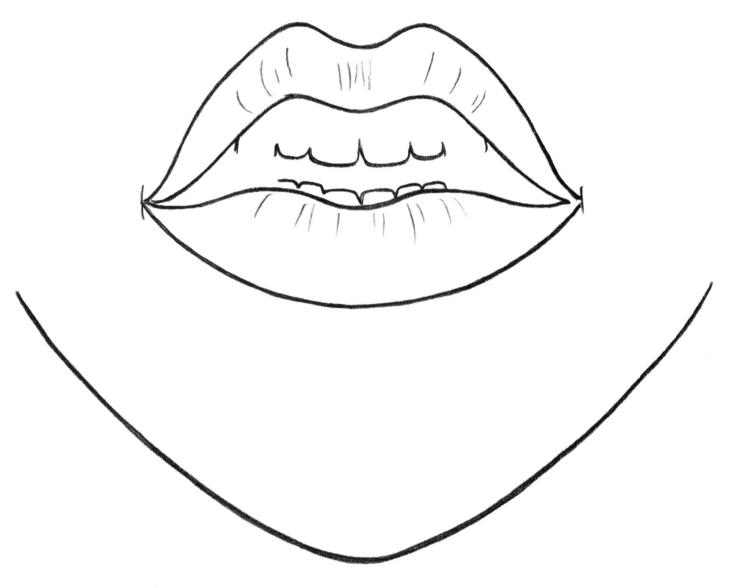

Quinn is
startled
TO SEE THE WOMAN
HAS FANGS

DRAW FANGS ON
THE WOMAN'S TEETH

THE WOMAN DOES NOT HAVE A REFLECTION IN A STAINED GLASS MIRROR

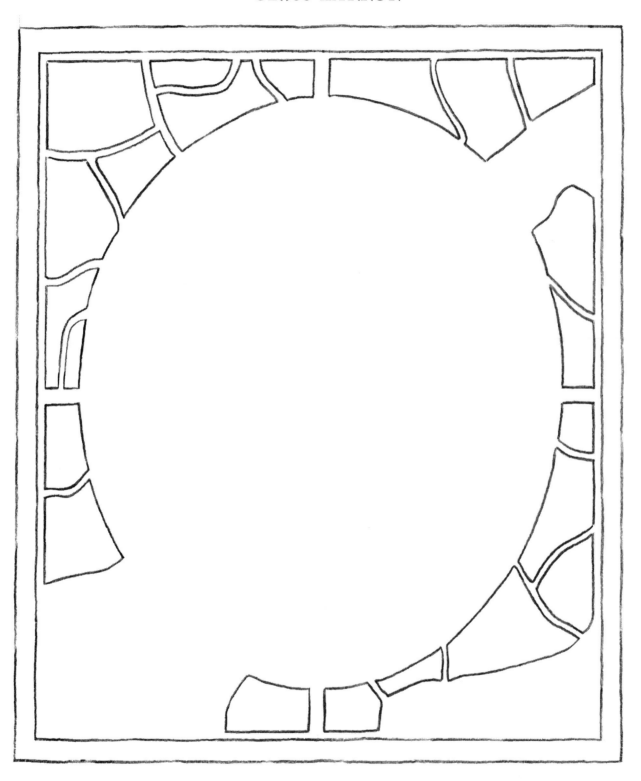

FINISH THE DESIGN ON THIS STAINED GLASS MIRROR

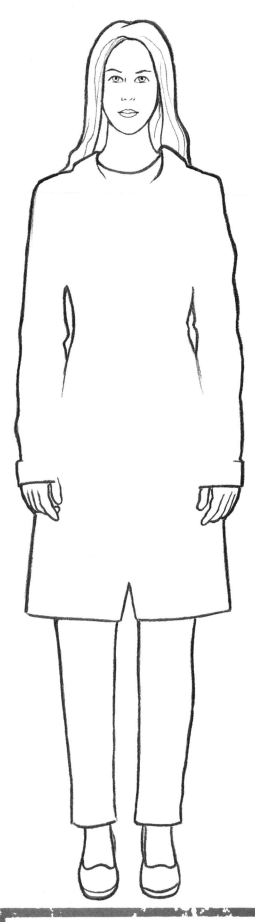

FINISH DETAILS ON HER COAT
ADD BATS FLUTTERING NEARBY

DRAW THE VAMPIRESS
WHO IS WEARING THIS CLOAK

Quinn is
confronted
BY MORE STRANGE
WOMEN

CREATE A NEW HAIRSTYLE

DRAW A WILD HAIRSTYLE

WHAT IS THE NAME OF THIS
CREEPY CEMETERY?

WRITE NAMES ON THE
HEADSTONES

THE full moon RISES AND BATS INVADE THE SKY.

FILL THE SKY WITH BATS

CREATE AN INSCRIPTION
ON THE GRAVESTONE

Quinn finds
Weapons
AT THE GRAVESITE ...

WOODEN STAKES...

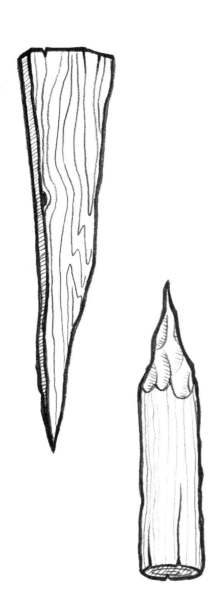

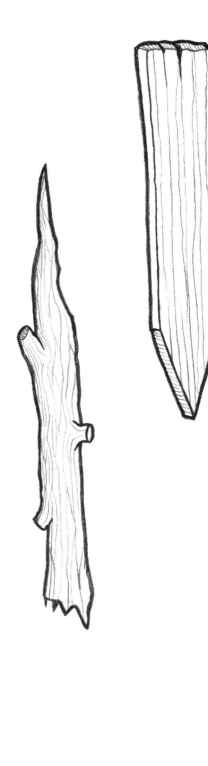

DOODLE MORE STAKES
FOR **Q**UINN TO USE

BOTTLES OF
HOLY WATER ...

ADD SOME DESIGNS
TO THE BOTTLES

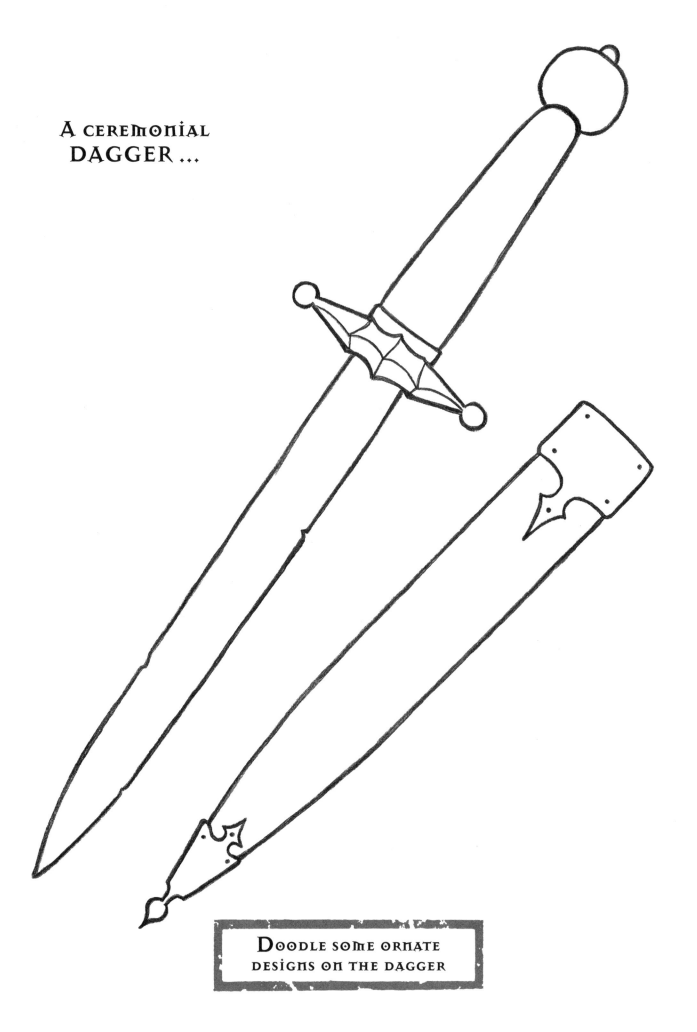

A ceremonial
DAGGER ...

DOODLE SOME ORNATE
DESIGNS ON THE DAGGER

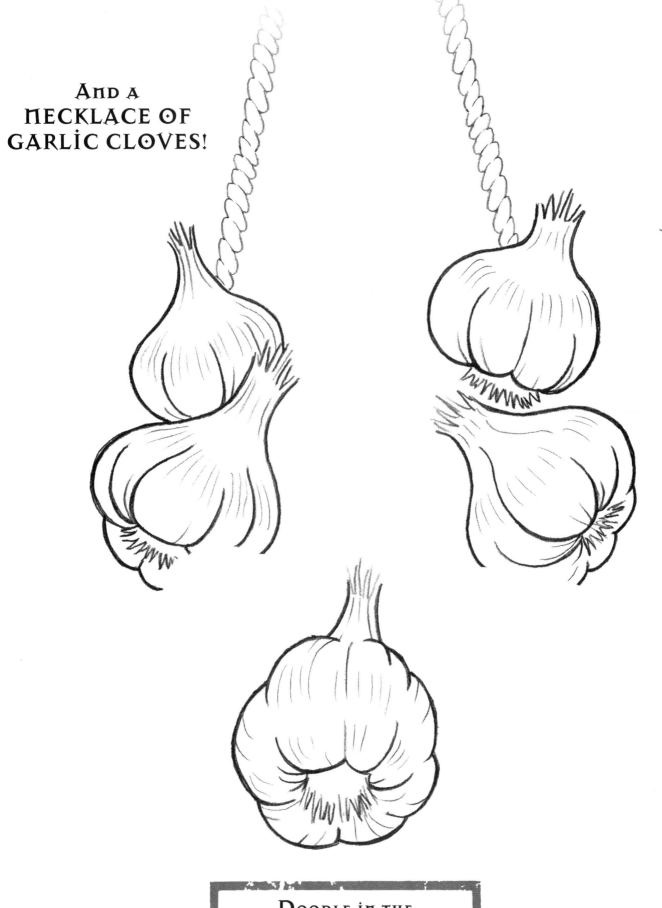

AND A
NECKLACE OF
GARLIC CLOVES!

DOODLE IN THE
MISSING PIECES OF GARLIC

MAKE THIS SCENE
EVEN SCARIER

HER LOCKET
BEGINS TO GLOW
WITH AN
Unearthly
LIGHT.

DRAW THE LOCKET WITH AN
EERIE GLOW AROUND IT

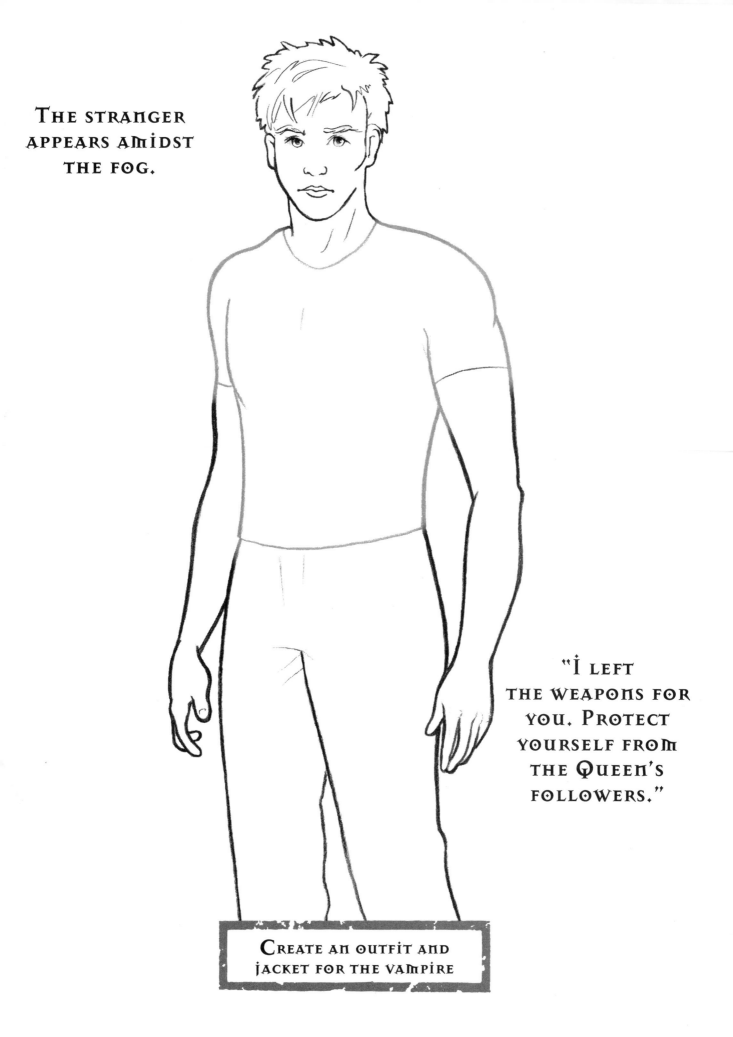

THE STRANGER APPEARS AMIDST THE FOG.

"I LEFT THE WEAPONS FOR YOU. PROTECT YOURSELF FROM THE QUEEN'S FOLLOWERS."

CREATE AN OUTFIT AND JACKET FOR THE VAMPIRE

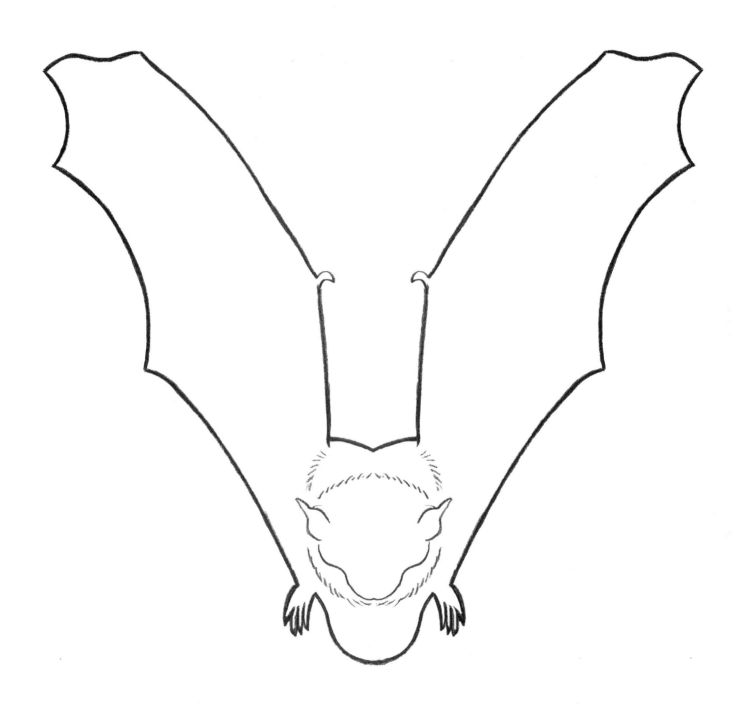

ADD DETAILS TO THE BAT

DOODLE MORE RAILINGS AND
SOME FOG IN THIS SCENE

THE FOG PARTS
AND A
CASTLE IS REVEALED

DRAW A PATH UP TO THE CASTLE
AND TREES ALONG THE EDGE

SKETCH IN SCARY DETAILS
ON THE DOOR

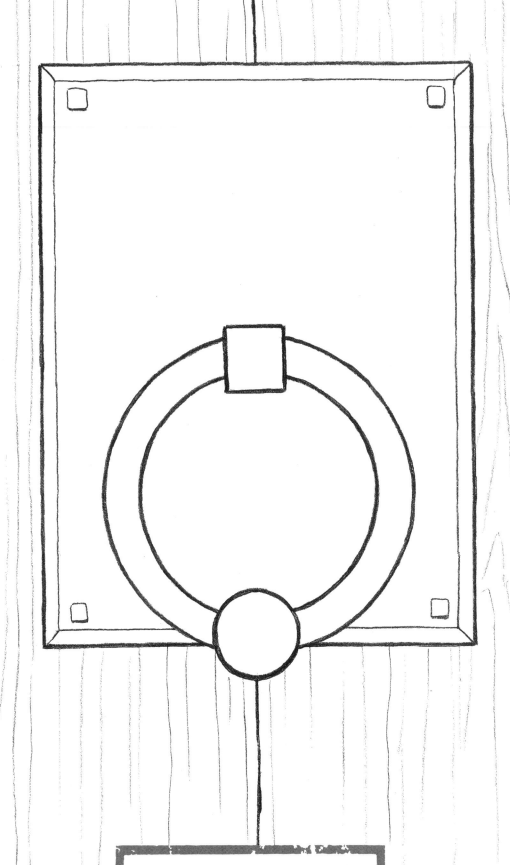

DECORATE THE DOOR KNOCKER

DOODLE A GHOSTLY FIGURE
PEERING OUT THIS WINDOW

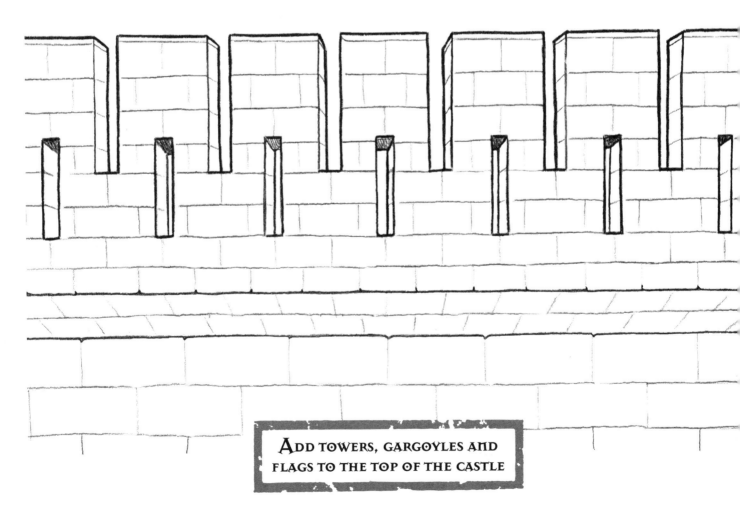

ADD TOWERS, GARGOYLES AND
FLAGS TO THE TOP OF THE CASTLE

CREATE A FLAG FLYING OVER THE CASTLE AND FINISH THE SKY

DECORATE THIS MYSTERIOUS
FIREPLACE AND BUILD A FIRE

ADD SOME SPOOKY BOOKS
TO THE SHELF

FINISH THE DETAILS ON
THE SUIT OF ARMOR

LIGHT AND DECORATE THIS
WALL SCONCE IN THE CASTLE

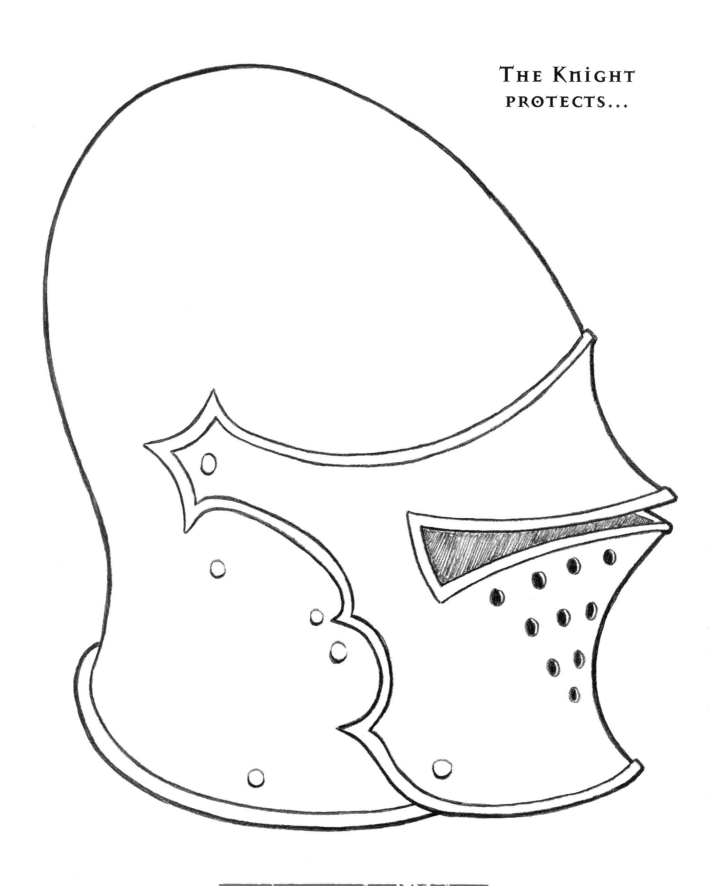

DOODLE MORE DETAILS
ON THE HELMET

...But the **Queen** holds the power!

Add more pieces to the chessboard

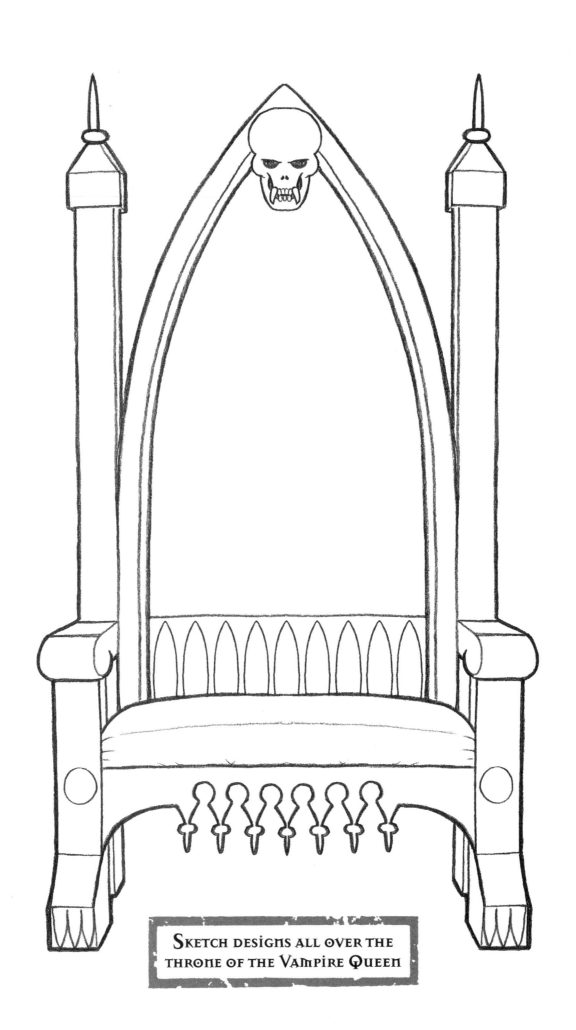

SKETCH DESIGNS ALL OVER THE
THRONE OF THE VAMPIRE QUEEN

DECORATE THE
VAMPIRE QUEEN'S CROWN

Jewels
FOR THE
Queen

ADD MORE ITEMS TO
THE QUEEN'S NECKLACE

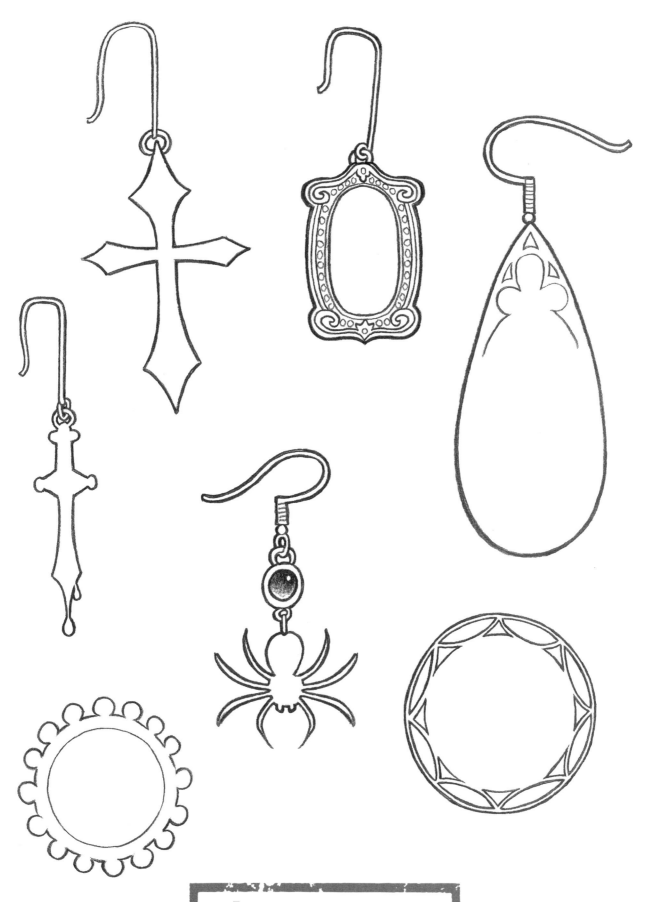

ADD SOME EERIE DETAILS
TO HER EARRINGS

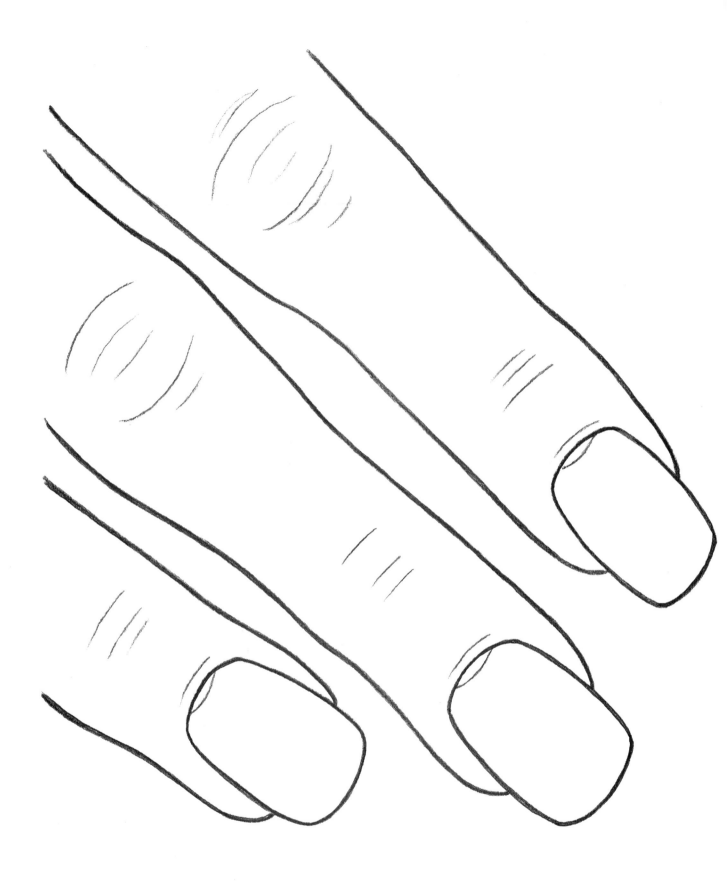

PAINT DESIGNS ON
HER FINGERNAILS

CREATE A DESIGN ON
THE QUEEN'S RING

DOODLE MORE JEWELRY IN
THE VAMPIRE QUEEN'S BOX

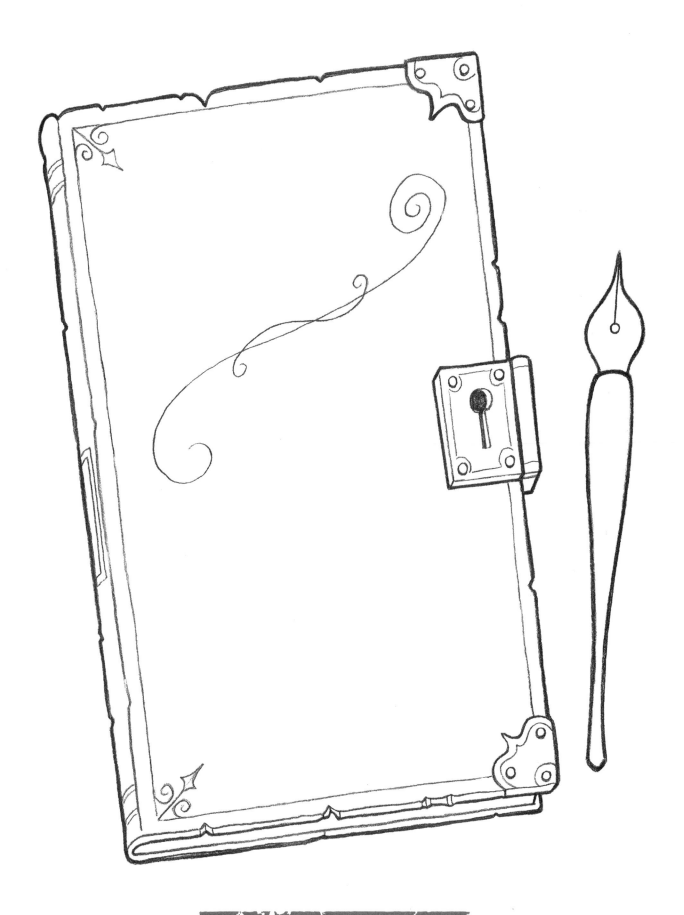

DECORATE THE COVER OF THE
VAMPIRE QUEEN'S DIARY

DOODLE GOTHIC DESIGNS ON
THE QUEEN'S CUP

ADD SPELLS TO THE
BOOK OF MAGIC

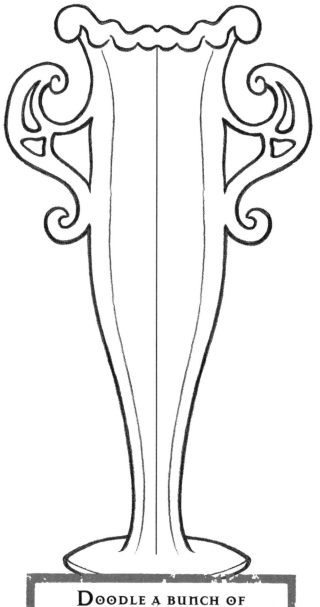

ADD ROSE PETALS TO THE STEMS

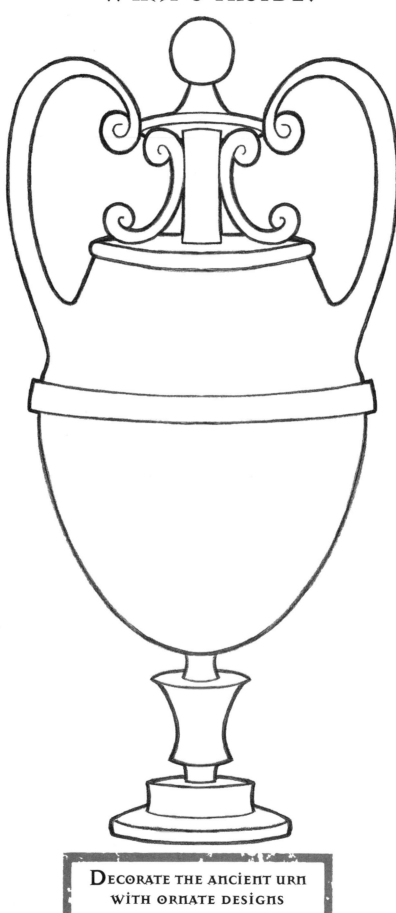

DECORATE THE ANCIENT URN
WITH ORNATE DESIGNS

WILL THESE UNLOCK THE CASTLE'S SECRETS?

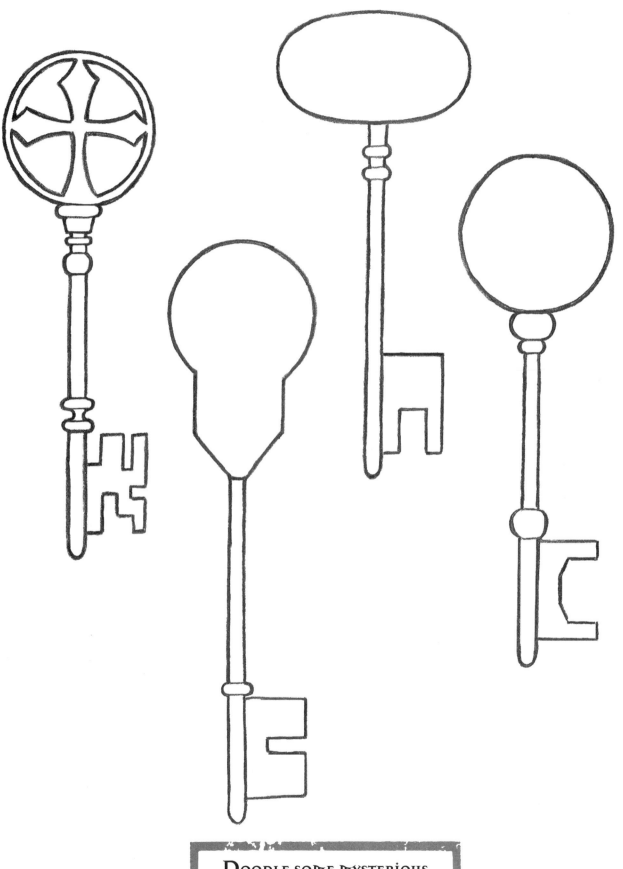

DOODLE SOME MYSTERIOUS
DETAILS ON THESE CREEPY KEYS

DRAW A CREATURE PEERING
OUT OF THE CLOSET…

NOW, DRAW THE CREATURE THAT
GOT OUT OF THE CLOSET

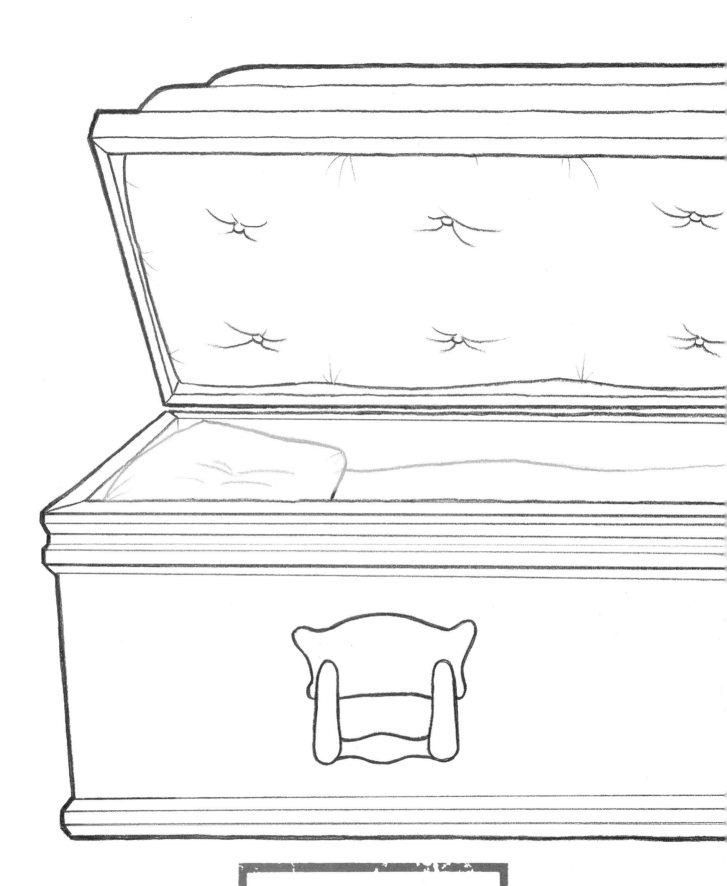

SKETCH A FIGURE IN THE COFFIN

WHO IS COMING DOWN
THE STAIRS?

ADD A FRIGHTFUL FACE TO
THIS PAINTING

DRAW A TREE FOR
THE RAVEN TO PERCH ON

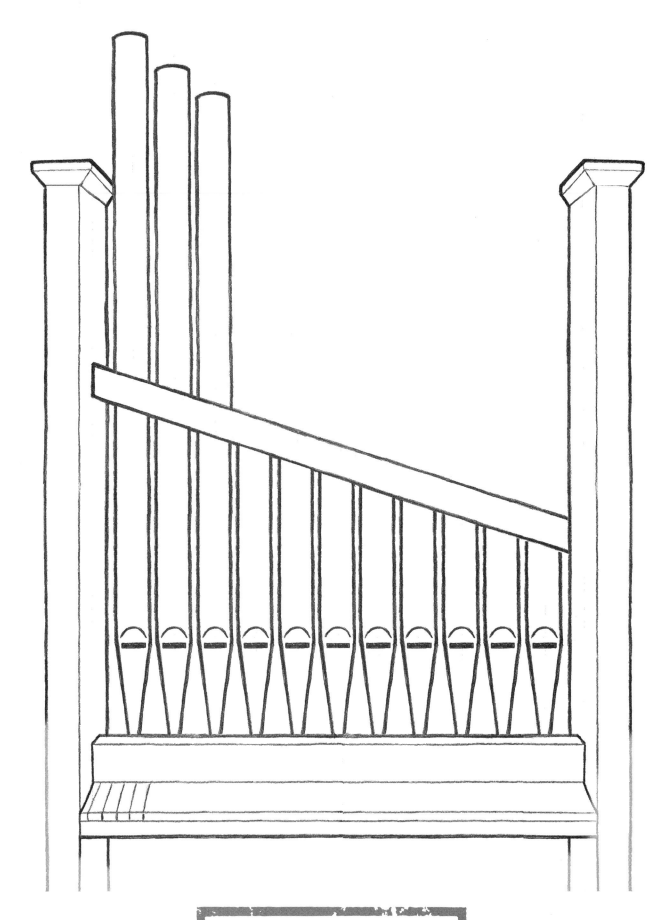

FINISH THE KEYS AND PIPES
ON THE ORGAN

Will Music
wake the
Dead?

DOODLE SOME CREEPY MUSICAL
NOTES COMING FROM THE ORGAN

It's the night for the Masquerade Ball...

DOODLE MORE DETAILS
ON THE MASK

IT'S A TIME OF DISGUISES AND DECEPTION

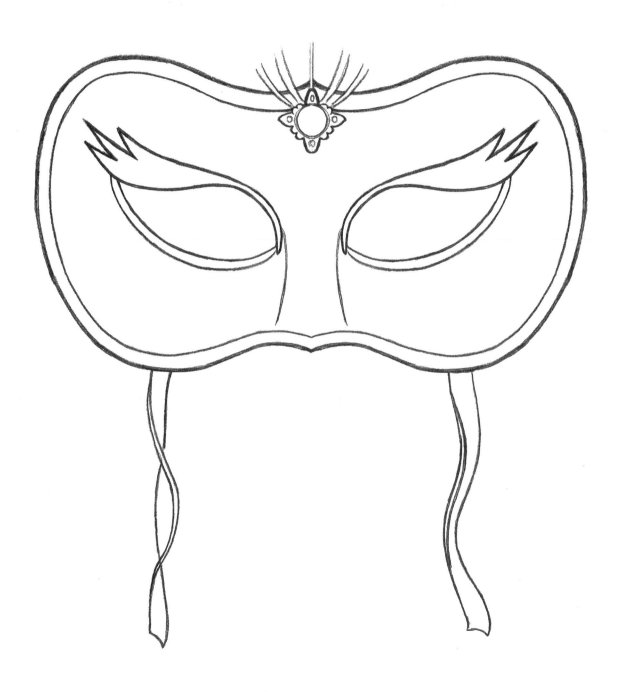

COMPLETE THE FACE
WEARING THIS MASK

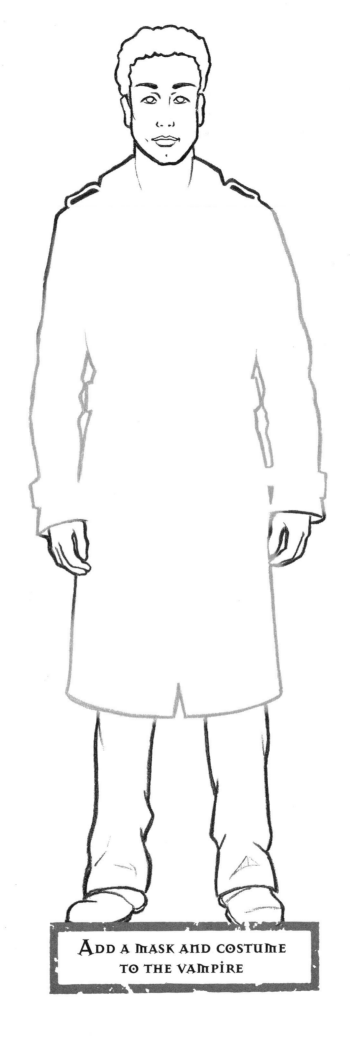

ADD A MASK AND COSTUME
TO THE VAMPIRE

DESIGN HER GOWN
FOR THE MASQUERADE

DRAW A SCARY FACE ON
THE RAG DOLL

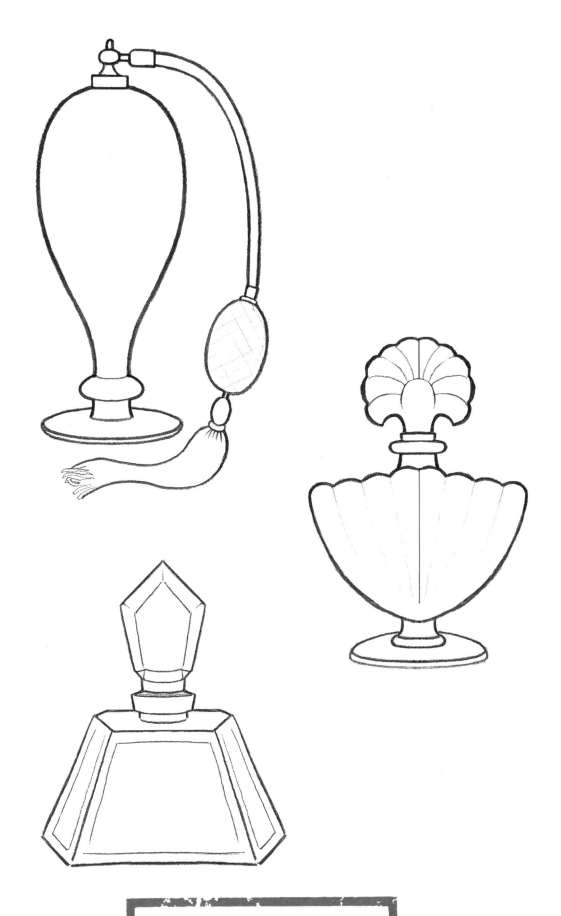

DESIGN LABELS FOR
THE PERFUME BOTTLES

DOODLE A GHOSTLY FIGURE
SITTING IN THIS CHAIR

ADD DRIPPING CANDLES
TO THE CANDELABRA

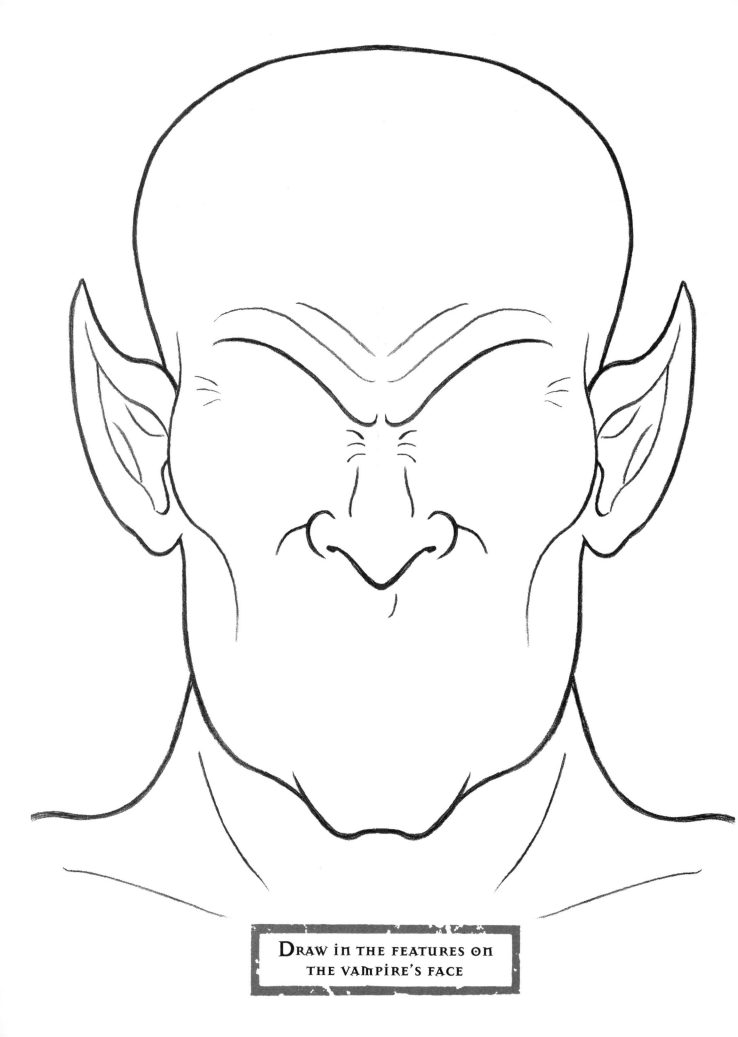

DRAW IN THE FEATURES ON
THE VAMPIRE'S FACE

THE VAMPIRE RISES AT MIDNIGHT

DESIGN THE WATCH AND
ADD A FOB TO THE CHAIN

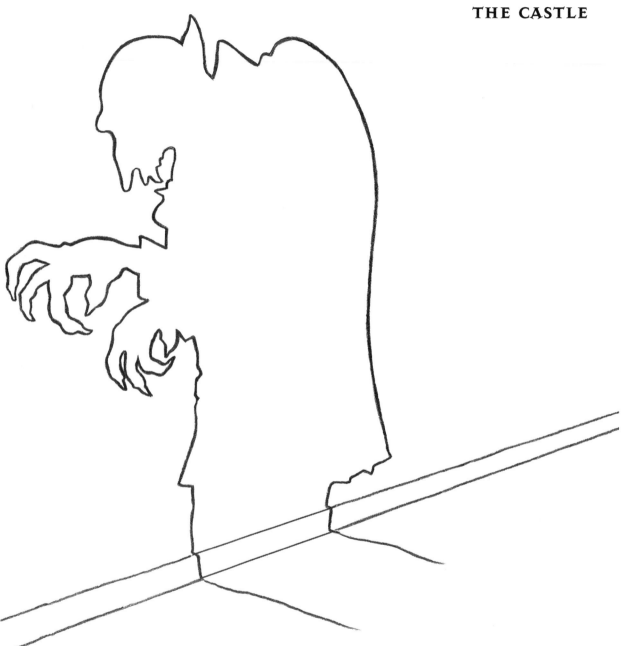

DOODLE THE CREATURE
CASTING THIS SHADOW

WHAT DEMONS MAY DANCE WITHIN THE FLAMES?

ADD FLAMES AND SMOKE IN
THE FIREPLACE

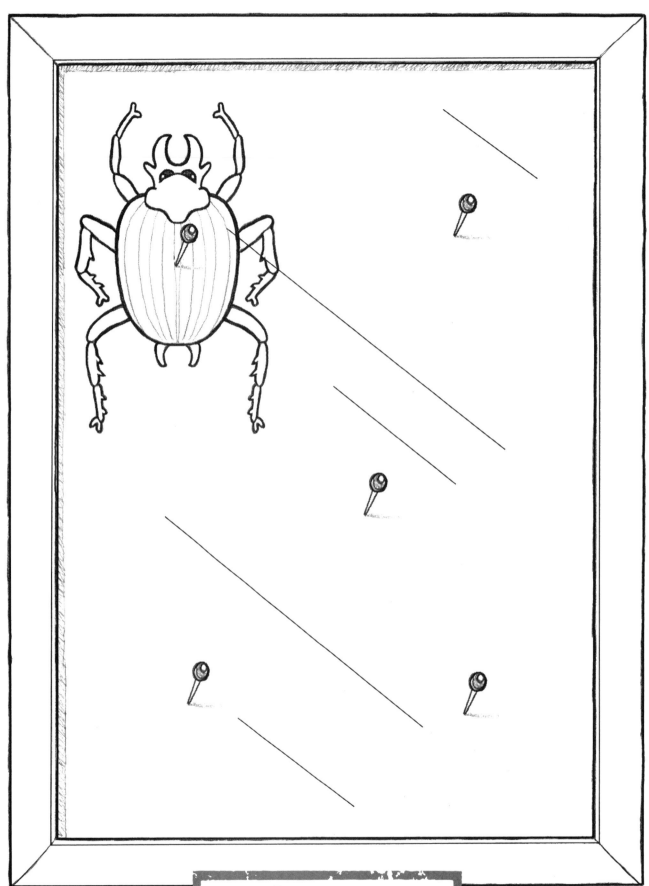

ADD BUGS TO
THIS INSECT COLLECTION

DRAW A FIGURE
INSIDE THE COFFIN

SKETCH SOME DECAYING FRUIT
INSIDE THIS BOWL

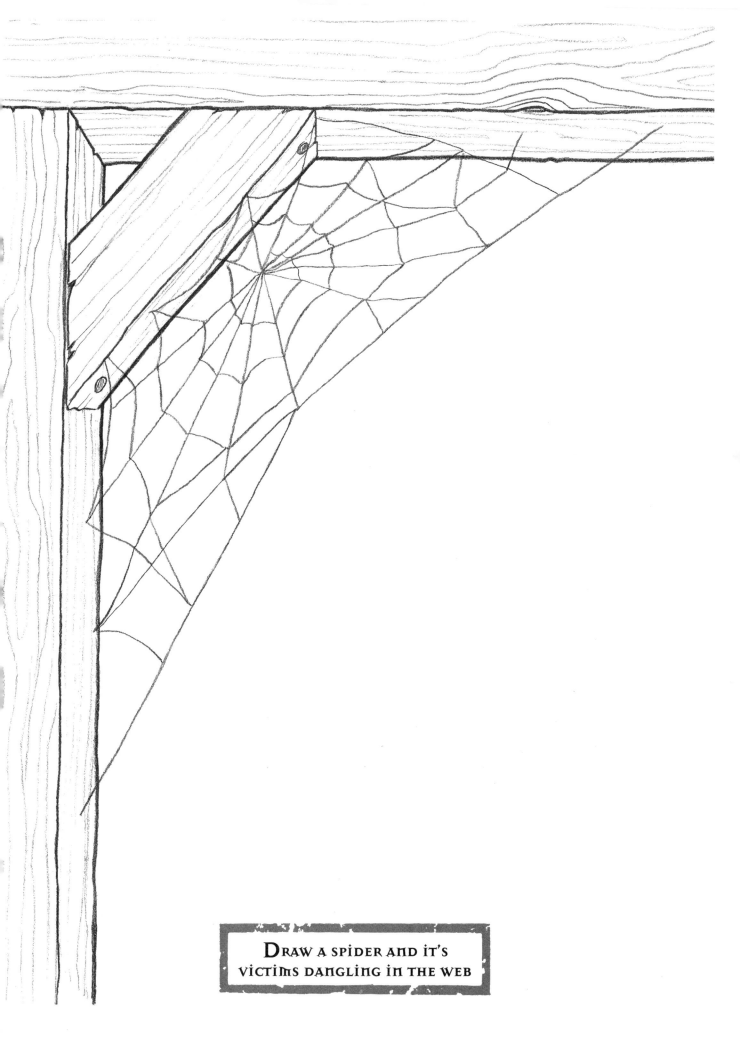

DRAW A SPIDER AND IT'S
VICTIMS DANGLING IN THE WEB

CREATE LABELS FOR
THE BOTTLES OF POTIONS

Eye of Bat

DOODLE A DEMON ESCAPING
FROM THE BOTTLE

A treat fit for a Creature

ADD SOME DECAY TO
THE QUEEN'S APPLE

WHO LIES IN THIS GRAVE?

WHAT IS REFLECTED IN THE
MIRROR? DRAW WHAT YOU SEE...

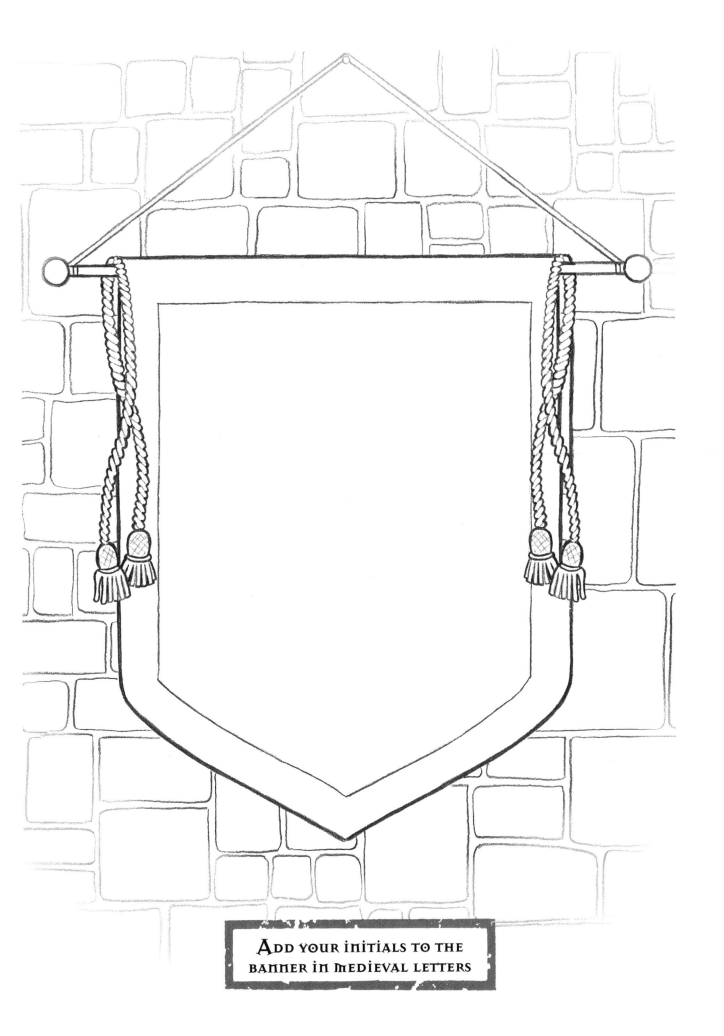

ADD YOUR INITIALS TO THE
BANNER IN MEDIEVAL LETTERS

SKETCH SOME ITEMS AND SCENES
IN THE ROOMS OF THE CASTLE

DOODLE IVY GROWING AROUND
THE WINDOW AND WHO'S INSIDE

For the
Thirst
of the Vampires

CREATE A LABEL FOR THIS
VIAL OF VAMPIRE BLOOD

DOODLE A BEARD ON THE MAN

DRAW A WEREWOLF HOWLING
AT THE FULL MOON

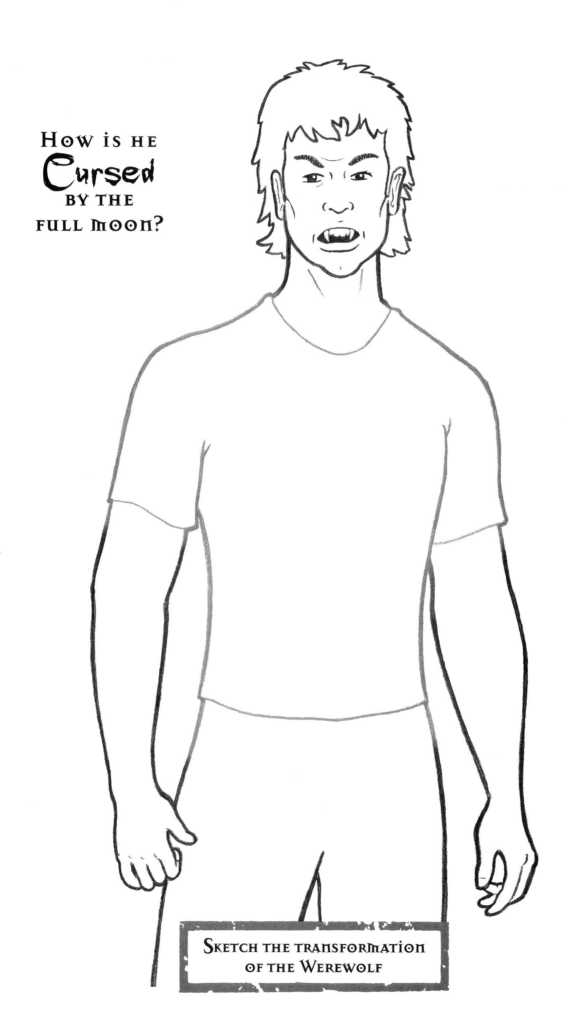

HOW IS HE **Cursed** BY THE FULL MOON?

SKETCH THE TRANSFORMATION OF THE WEREWOLF

CREATE A WOLF HEAD CREST IN
THE MIDDLE OF THE SHIELD

SHOW THE WEREWOLF
BARING HIS FANGS

Who is watching the night skies?

ADD EYES AND TALONS TO THE OWL

FINISH DRAWING THE BRANCHES
AND LEAVES ON THE TREE

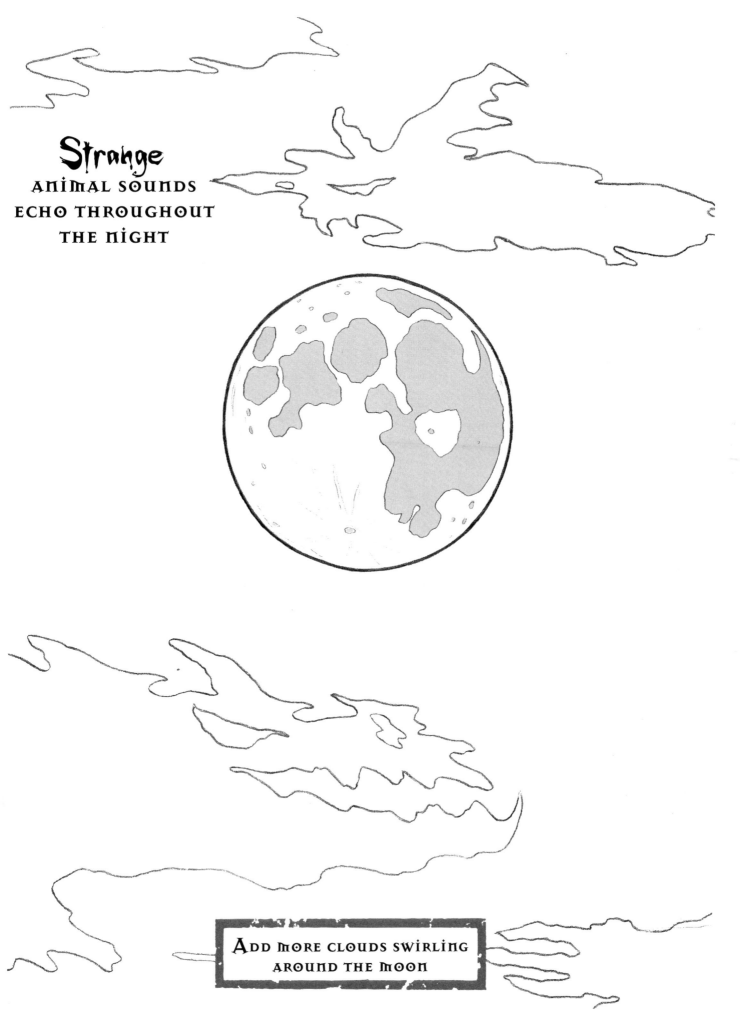

Strange animal sounds echo throughout the night

Add more clouds swirling around the moon

DRAW THE CLAWS APPEARING
ON THE WEREWOLF'S HAND

FINISH THE BEARD ON
THE WEREWOLF

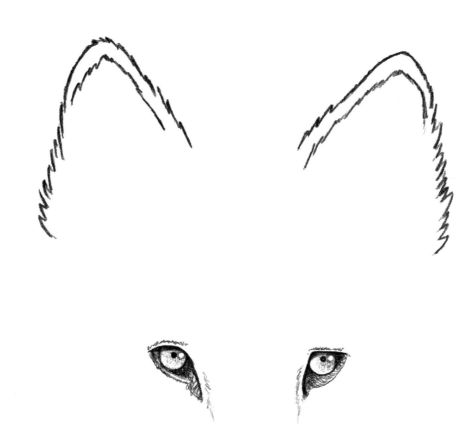

FINISH THE WOLF HEAD
AND ADD PART OF HIS BODY

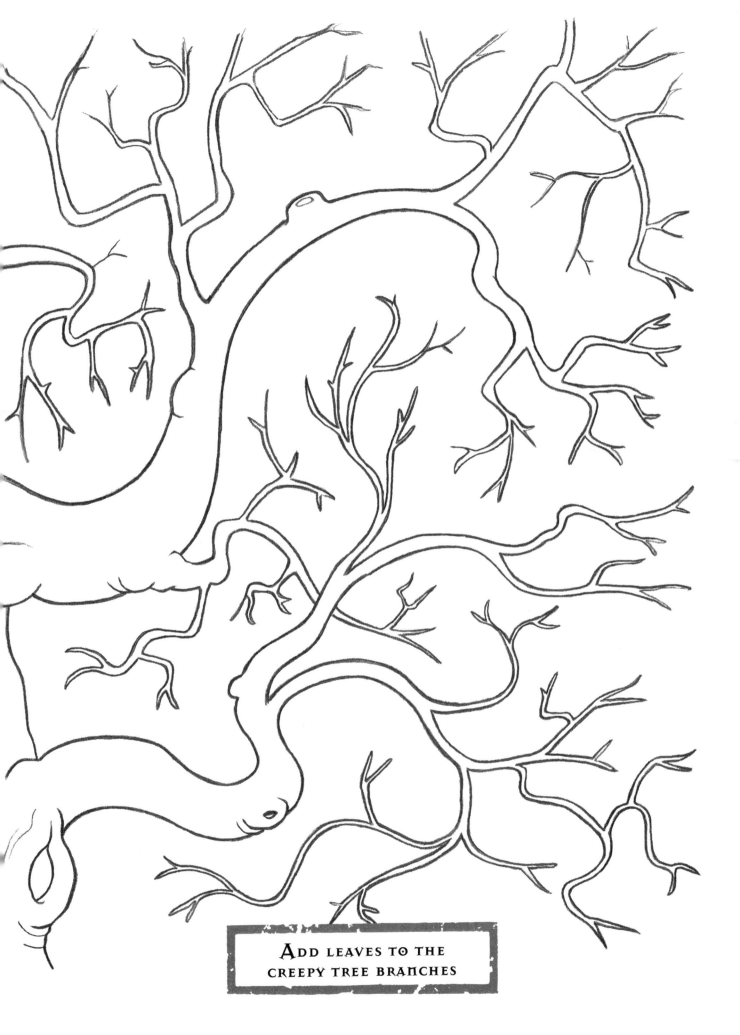

ADD LEAVES TO THE
CREEPY TREE BRANCHES

ADD HAIRSTYLES TO
THE FEMALE SILHOUETTES

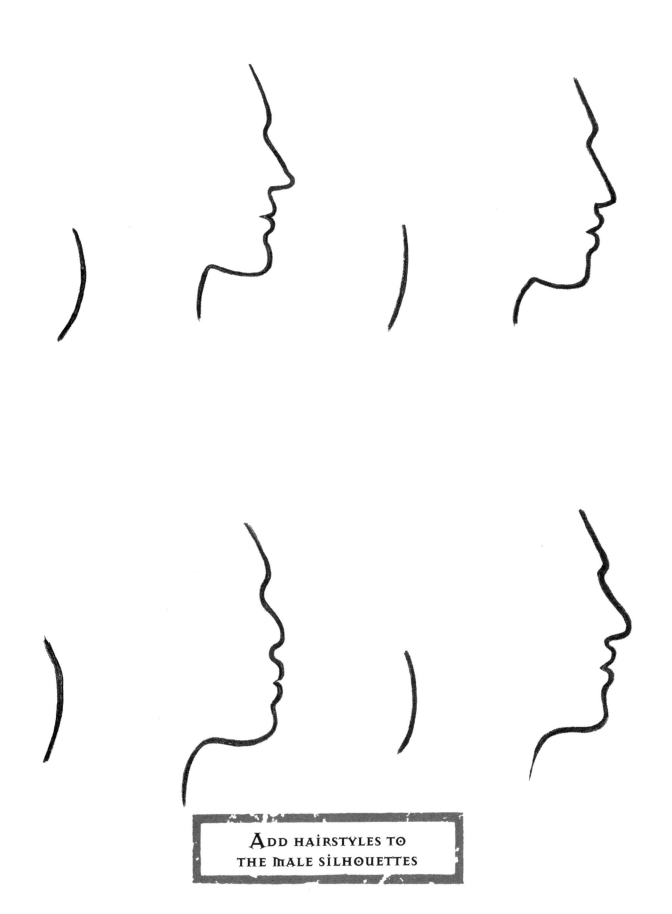

ADD HAIRSTYLES TO
THE MALE SILHOUETTES

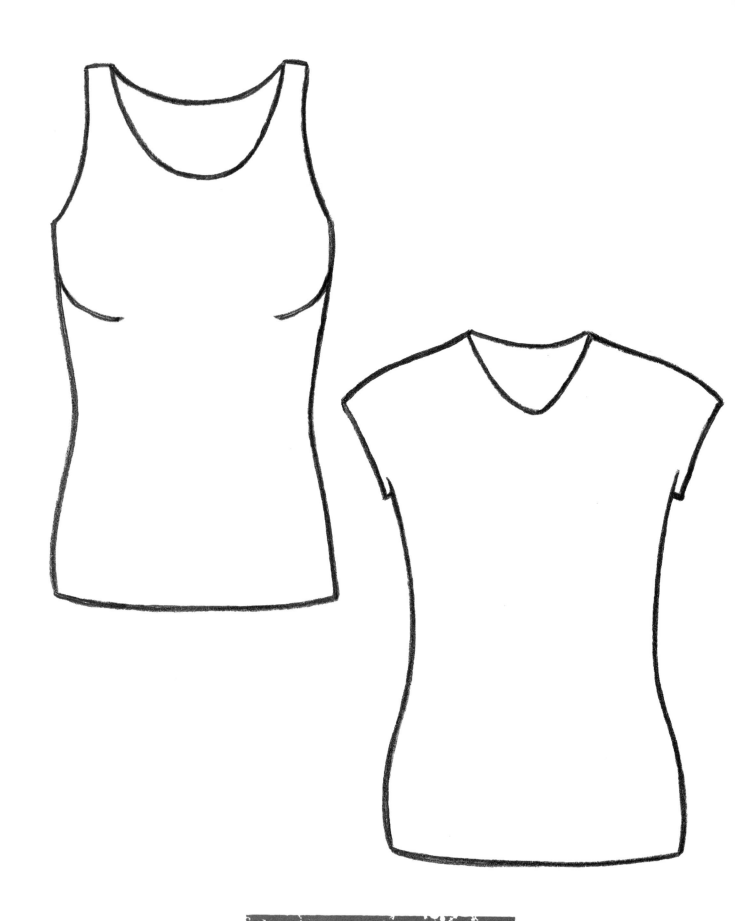

CREATE SOME INTERESTING
CLOTHING DESIGNS

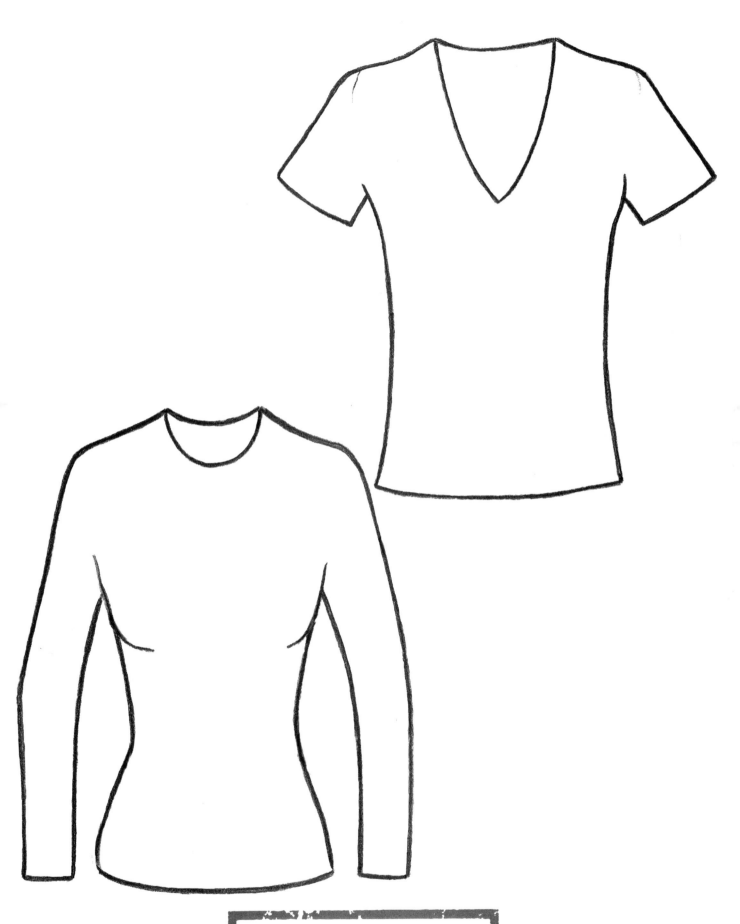

CREATE SOME INTERESTING
CLOTHING DESIGNS

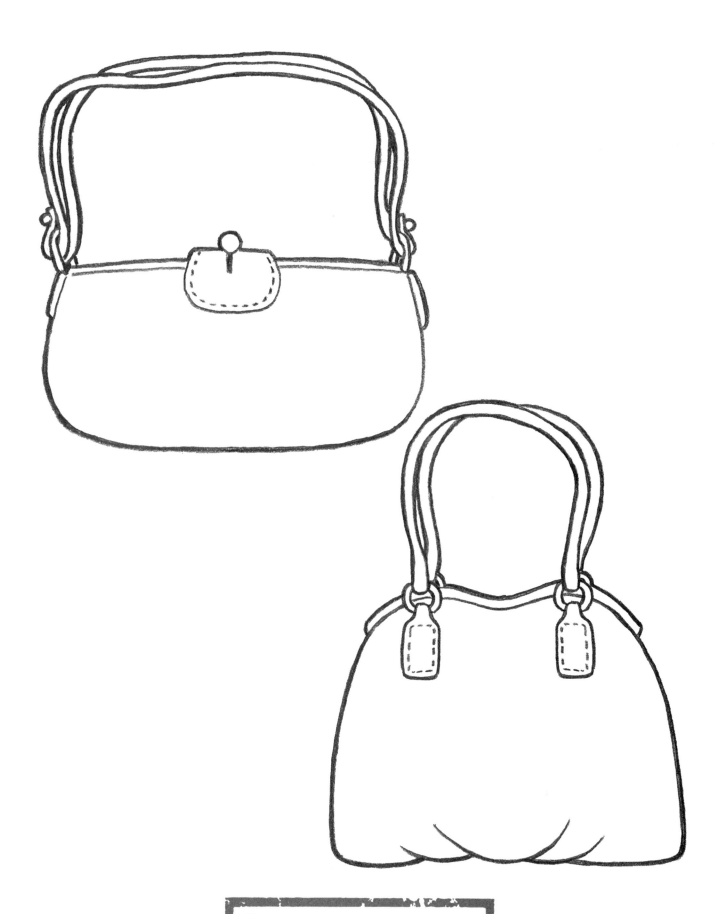

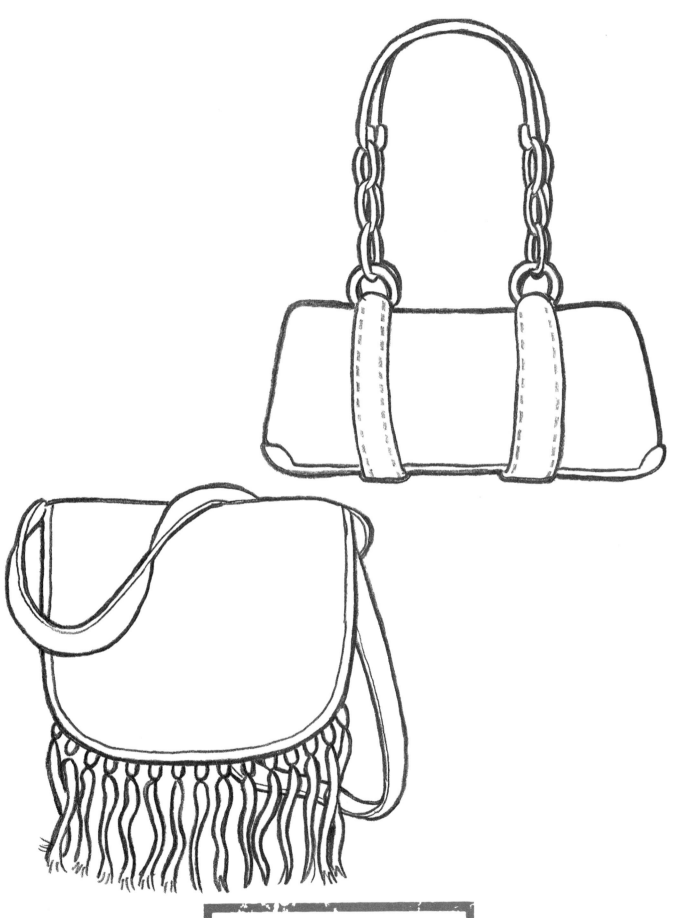

DOODLE PATTERNS AND DESIGNS
ON THE BAGS

DESIGN THE MINI DRESS

BUT
IF VAMPIRES ARE
ABOUT, IS IT A DATE
WITH DARKNESS?

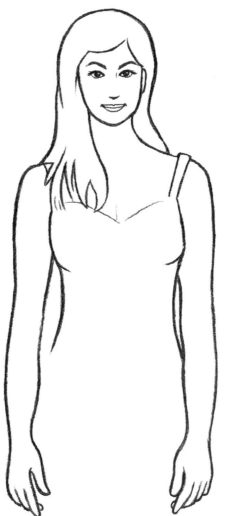

FINISH DESIGNING THE GOWN

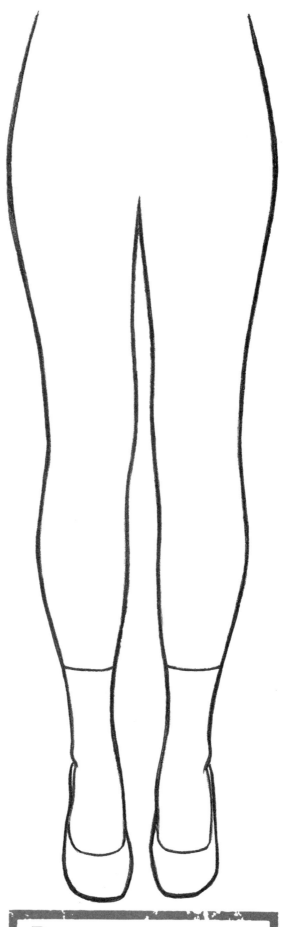

DOODLE SOME DESIGNS ON
HER LEGGINGS AND SHOES

ADD YOUR FAVORITE TEAM'S
LOGO TO HER OUTFIT

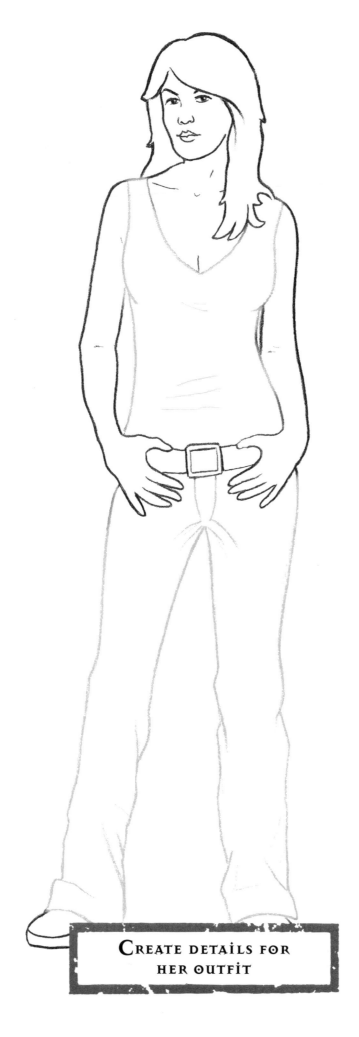

CREATE DETAILS FOR
HER OUTFIT

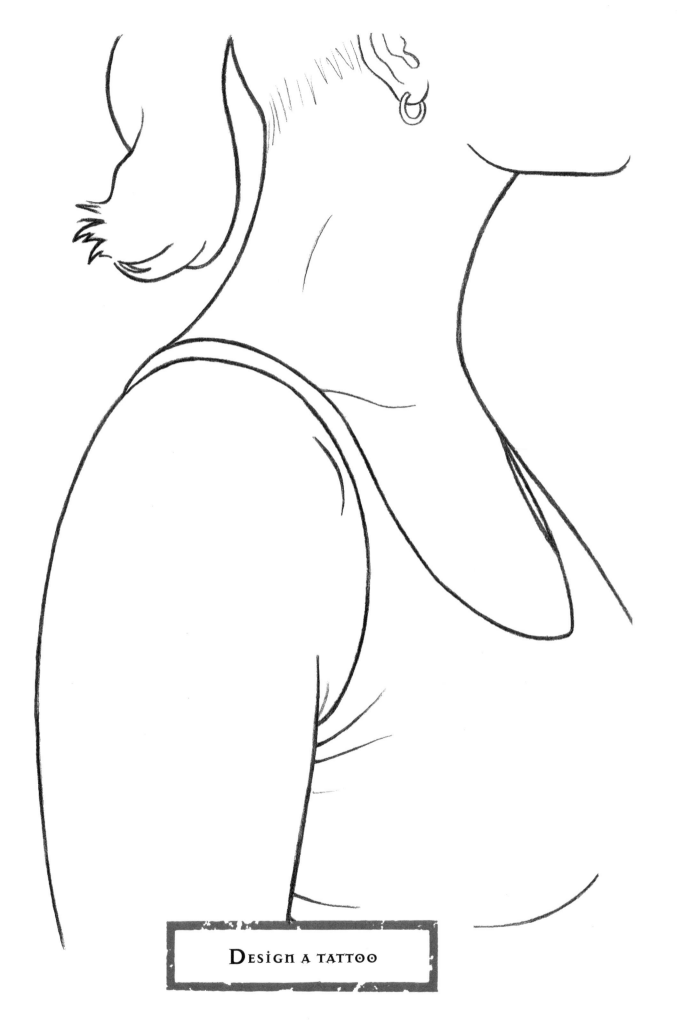

DESIGN A TATTOO

THIS VAMPIRE **Stalks** THE NIGHT FOR VICTIMS TO TRANSFORM

DRAW A MOUTH ON THIS FEROCIOUS VAMPIRE

SHE DOES NOT
SUSPECT THAT
danger
IS WAITING
TO POUNCE

CREATE SOME PATTERNS
ON THE DRESS

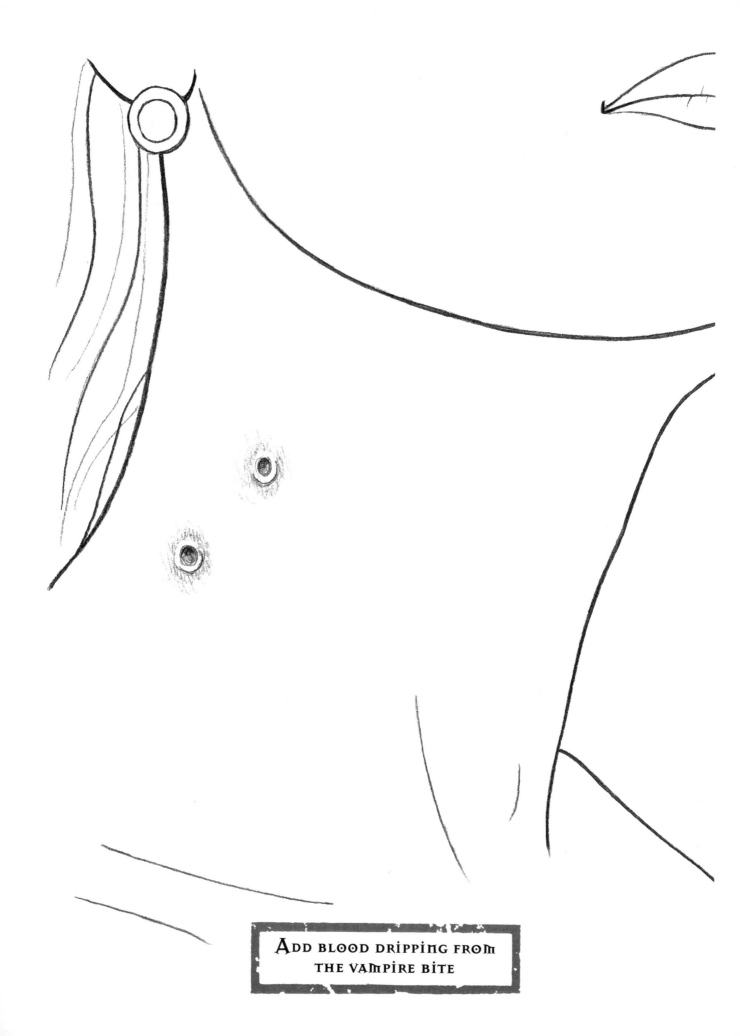

ADD BLOOD DRIPPING FROM
THE VAMPIRE BITE

TURN THE GIRL INTO
A TERRIFYING VAMPIRE

DOODLE IN THE FACIAL FEATURES
ON THE VAMPIRE

SKETCH THE ENTIRE FIGURE OF
THE TRANSFORMED VAMPIRE

CREATE A SIGN FOR
A FORTUNE TELLER'S BUSINESS

Can this Crystal Ball show the future?

DRAW A VISION IN
THE CRYSTAL BALL

WHAT FORTUNES ARE EMBROIDERED ON THESE PILLOWS?

DRAW SOME DESIGNS ON
THESE PILLOWS

DOODLE SOME CREEPY
ORNAMENTS ON THE WREATH

FINISH THE DETAILS ON
THE HEARSE

SKETCH SOME SCARY FACES IN
THE CAR WINDOWS

OH NO!...now You ARE TURNING INTO A VAMPIRE!

DRAW YOURSELF AS A VAMPIRE!